Macmillan Building and Surveying Series

Series Editor: Ivor H. Seeley
Emeritus Professor, Nottingham Trent University

(continued)

Property Finance David Isaac
Property Valuation Techniques David Isaac and Terry Steley
Public Works Engineering Ivor H. Seeley
Resource Management for Construction M.R. Canter
Quality Assurance in Building Alan Griffith
Quantity Surveying Practice Ivor H. Seeley
Recreation Planning and Development Neil Ravenscroft
Resource and Cost Control in Building Mike Canter
Small Building Works Management Alan Griffith
Structural Detailing, second edition P. Newton
Sub-Contracting under the JCT Standard Forms of Building Contract Jennie Price
Urban Land Economics and Public Policy, fifth edition P.N. Balchin, J.L. Kieve and
    G.H. Bull
Urban Regeneration R. Just and D. Williams
Urban Renewal – Theory and Practice Chris Couch
1980 JCT Standard Form of Building Contract, second edition R.F. Fellows
Value Management in Construction B. Norton and W. McElligott

Estimating, Tendering and Bidding for Construction

Theory and Practice

Adrian J. Smith

Department of Building and Construction
City University of Hong Kong

MACMILLAN

First published 1995 by
MACMILLAN PRESS LTD
Houndmills, Basingstoke, Hampshire RG21 2XS
and London
Companies and representatives
throughout the world

ISBN 0–333–62794–6

A catalogue record for this book is available
from the British Library

10 9 8 7 6 5 4 3 2 1
04 03 02 01 00 99 98 97 96 95

Typeset by Ian Kingston Editorial Services, Nottingham

Printed in Great Britain by Antony Rowe Ltd, Chippenham, Wiltshire

Contents

Preface

This book is about the twin processes of estimating and tendering for construction work. Unlike many other texts on the same subject it is not intended to be a compendium of estimators' labour constants, neither does it set out to describe in minute detail the calculation of unit rates for every construction trade. Although the mechanics of the estimating and tendering process are considered, they are considered only in sufficient detail for the general principles to be understood in the context of the process as a whole. Instead, this book attempts to explore estimating and tendering as a holistic process in the wider context of construction management and construction economics.

The objectives of this book are therefore twofold: firstly to provide a text covering rather wider aspects of estimating and tendering than has normally been the case in the past, and secondly to review recent research in the light of its application to UK estimating and tendering practice. In this respect I have drawn upon research published in various parts of the world, including the UK, America, Australia and Hong Kong.

The book is primarily aimed at those students who already have a basic grounding in the mechanics of estimating. It covers a wide range of subjects and I am well aware that some areas are treated more superficially than others. This is partly deliberate and partly imposed by pressures of space, but I have attempted to give extensive references wherever possible, in the hope that these might stimulate and assist the research of those wishing to pursue aspects of the subject to a greater depth. I hope the book might also be of interest to practitioners in the field.

Hong Kong   Adrian Smith
December 1994

1 Estimating and Tendering – Some Contextual Factors

1.1 INTRODUCTION

⌐Most construction works are let on the basis of some form of competition, in which the quoted price for the work usually plays a large part. It is therefore obvious that, for a construction company to thrive, it must have the ability to forecast the likely cost of proposed construction work, and thus at least be able to establish a baseline figure from which a price can be quoted to the client.⌐

The twin processes of estimating and tendering are thus very important, but before considering them in detail it will be useful to look at some of the contextual factors which govern the environment in which the construction company has to operate, and in doing so gain a feel for some of the problems involved. These factors will include the organisation of the construction industry, the nature of construction clients and the way construction work is procured, and the economic framework within which the constituent firms operate.

1.2 THE CONSTRUCTION INDUSTRY

The construction industry throughout the world is, in many ways, unique in economic terms. Briscoe (1988, p. 10), for example, says:

> While there are many economic characteristics which the construction industry experiences in common with other sectors, there remain a number of features which set it apart.

The same view is expressed slightly differently by Hillebrandt (1984, p. 1):

> …the construction industry has characteristics that separately are shared by other industries but in combination appear in construction alone.

The industry is also very diverse. In terms of its constituent firms, at the lowest end of the scale it is essentially local in character, with large numbers

1

of very small firms concentrating mainly on domestic scale work, generally repairs and renovations. It then runs through a continuum of progressively larger organisations to very large international construction companies operating all over the world. Construction is also characterised by a high degree of specialisation, with many firms specialising in specific parcels of work, although the products of the industry as a whole, the completed construction projects, are more often bought by clients as complete entities. During the production phase this situation gives rise to the need for a management layer, the main contractor, whose major task is to integrate, control and coordinate all of the various inputs required in order to deliver the whole completed construction project to the client.

A further distinction is that, compared with most other industries, the individual products of the construction industry are relatively few in number, but each is of comparatively high value, and, despite various attempts over the years towards standardisation, virtually all major construction projects are to a large extent, individual bespoke solutions to particular and specific problems. Every separate construction project is carried out on a different site, and it is likely that each site will pose different problems for the construction contractor in terms of access, geography, geology, working conditions etc. Each construction site becomes, in effect, a temporary 'factory', the purpose of which is to produce the very restricted range of products comprising the particular construction project, and which is then dismantled and removed on completion of the work.

The temporary nature of the production facility, and the fact that each project is a unique solution to a particular problem, also gives rise to 'people problems'. In many cases the people involved in the design and construction processes will be different from one construction project to another. In other words, the construction 'team' must be formed anew for each new project, and must very quickly go through all of the usual 'team-building' processes if it is to operate as an efficient working organisation.

All of these factors pose considerable problems for the contractor when attempting to fix a price for construction work. Although some commentators (e.g. Adrian, 1982), have seen construction contractors as a part of manufacturing industry, there are in fact marked differences. Unlike most other industries, the uniqueness of construction projects and the temporary nature of the organisations required to complete them give rise to considerable uncertainty when attempting to forecast what the cost of the works will actually be.

1.3   THE CONSTRUCTION CLIENT

In addition to the problems posed by the uniqueness of each of the industry's products, the construction contractor must also cope with the problems posed by the fact that construction is an industry which is essentially client-led. Most construction projects arise as a direct result of prospective clients approaching the industry rather than as a result of the industry marketing its products. This is not to say that individual firms do not market themselves; they obviously do, but the marketing is generally intended to differentiate the service offered by them from others in the field, to persuade clients who have already decided that they may need the services of the industry to select their particular company instead of others in the same field, rather than to persuade the general public to buy the products the industry produces. The major exception to this, and the closest the construction industry gets to mass production and a large consumer market, is in speculative housing, but even then total sales to each customer will be small, with little opportunity for repeat business.

The construction industry has many different types of client, ranging from 'experienced' clients with a detailed and intimate knowledge of the construction industry and with large and ongoing programmes of work (e.g. government and other public authorities) through to those 'naïve' clients, often private individuals, who may build only occasionally; maybe only once in their lives. Clients embark on construction work for different reasons. Examples might include property or development companies looking for investment or to make a profit from the sale or letting of completed buildings, industrial and commercial clients looking to provide themselves with facilities for carrying out their business, private individuals looking to provide themselves with somewhere to live, and public sector clients looking to procure public works. Although each of these different types of client has different motives for building, and all therefore have their different priorities and differing expectations of the construction industry, they do all have some things in common:

1. To every client the particular construction project is usually extremely important. Powell (1980, p. 1) puts it rather well:

> Every building ever built arose from a carefully premeditated decision which was usually of the utmost importance to the person who made it.

2. For most clients any construction work represents a large investment in both time and money.

3. All clients rely to a greater or lesser extent on the construction team (the contractors and consultants) that they employ to solve their problems for them. Experienced clients, that is those who build regularly and have considerable experience of the construction industry, may often, although not by any means always, be able to analyse and articulate their problems for themselves, but on the other hand, especially in the case of those naïve clients who have little or no experience of construction, the role of the

construction team will also include helping them to identify what their problems actually are.⟩ `

4. No matter how good the drawings and the models are, many clients, even some of the most experienced, will have difficulty in visualising what the completed project will look like and how well it will work, and therefore how likely it is that it will actually meet their needs, until the project is constructed.

In addition, because construction is a costly and lengthy process, each construction project is essentially a 'one shot' activity. Each and every construction project has only one chance to satisfy the client, and yet a number of studies over the years have purported to show that the construction industry in general, and in particular in the UK, has a poor record in this respect. Fine (1987), for example, while admittedly presenting a somewhat extreme view, still paints a disturbing picture:

> …the estimating and planning tools in use in the construction industry, for the last few score of years, are failing too regularly for comfort…. Almost every major project fails: Motorways, Ports, Tunnels, Dams, Power Utilities, Ships, Military Installations, Space Stations, Aircraft and Chemical Plants fail to be completed according to estimate. This is not an English disease. This is a world catastrophe.

While things have undoubtedly improved in recent years, there is still a strong likelihood that the completed work will either be late and/or will cost more than the client was originally led to believe.⟨There are, in some parts of the world, considerable problems with quality control, and there is even a possibility that the completed work may fail in some way to satisfy the client's functional needs. If the completed project does seriously fail to satisfy the client's needs it will almost certainly be very difficult and very costly to make necessary modifications.

Construction clients also demand progressively shorter contract periods, thus leading to the need for a greater degree of pre-contract planning by contractors. Unfortunately, however, this same time pressure also tends to mean that in many cases the pre-contract design work is incomplete at the time tenders are invited. In addition to adding to the degree of uncertainty posed by the project from the construction contractor's point of view, this often gives rise to the need for variations during the course of the work. These are extremely disruptive, particularly when the contractor is working to a tight time-scale, and consequently often give rise to expensive claims for additional payment. Clients are not likely to be very pleased if, on completion of the project, they are asked to pay large sums of money as a result of variations which were necessary because of problems which were avoidable at the design stage.

In the light of all of the above, the prime objective of all construction clients ought to be to seek to maximise the chances that the construction team they choose will be able to offer the best possible solution to their problem in terms of their particular required combination of functional performance, time, cost and quality. Although each of these four criteria will carry different weight for particular clients on particular schemes, it is likely that in their attempts to secure the best all-round solution most clients will want to compare several different alternatives, and this then implies some form of competition. It is perhaps unfortunate, but nonetheless a fact, that on many, perhaps the majority of, projects in the past this competition has been largely limited to price, with a number of contractors each submitting bids for the work and the winning contractor usually being the one who has submitted the lowest price.

In the past competition has tended to be limited to the construction contract itself, with professional firms (architects, engineers, quantity surveyors etc.) being appointed to carry out the pre-contract work on the basis of some generally agreed scale of fees, but more recently it has become the norm for clients to seek competitive fee bids from their professional consultants as well.

In the light of the above, it is apparent that, in addition to the problems of project uniqueness mentioned above, construction contractors submitting competitive tenders also have to cope with the demands of a commercial market place. The problems and risks are obvious, but Park (1979, p. 37) sums up the problems rather well:

> Under the competitive bidding system, the contractor is forced to make a 'short sale' of his resources. In effect he is selling a finished commodity – a building for example – which he does not yet have and which does not even exist at the time the sale is made. The contractor is gambling that he will, within a prescribed time, be able to furnish the end product at the price originally set.

It might therefore be appropriate to look briefly at the economics of the construction market.

1.4   ECONOMICS OF THE CONSTRUCTION MARKET

In general economic terms the construction market is characterised by a large number of sellers (i.e. construction firms) competing for a comparatively small number of relatively high-value orders, and it is a characteristic of this type of market that prices tend, in the main, to be market-led.

Given a perfect market, economic theory tells us that a further characteristic of competitive markets of this type would be that the market mechanism is essentially self-regulating, i.e. if there are too many firms chasing too few orders then prices will tend to fall. Eventually, the less efficient will fail to secure enough work at a price which enables them to remain profitable, and if this situation continues they will leave the industry. This process will, in theory, continue until the number of firms in the market-place, the market price and the amount of work available are again in balance. Conversely, if the demand for construction services exceeds available capacity then prices and hence profit levels will be seen to rise and more firms will be attracted to enter the market until the *status quo* is again reached.

In the construction industry, however, such perfect market conditions rarely if ever apply, and the market does not therefore behave in precisely the way that the economic theory predicts that it should. One of the main reasons for this is that construction is a long-term business. Even for so-called 'fast track' projects, the time-scale for most major construction work, from the initial inception and feasibility study, through final completion and occupation of the building, to completion of the final account is likely to be measured in years.

The construction market as a whole therefore has considerable kinetic energy, and assuming a policy of non-intervention by government, in general tends to lag behind movements in the economy as a whole. The effect of this is that, in a recession, the construction sector may still appear to be strong and moving ahead even though the remainder of the economy is slowing down, and conversely when the economy as a whole begins to recover the lengthy lead times required to commence major construction projects results in construction appearing to be weak when the economy as a whole appears to be gaining momentum.

Given these circumstances it is very difficult for the construction market to adjust quickly to changes in demand. Note the need here to distinguish between 'demand' and 'need'. While there might appear to be an obvious need for considerable construction in order to improve social and living conditions in many parts of the world, the need will only be translated into an economic demand for the construction industry when someone is willing to pay for the work.

While the fragmented nature of the industry does, to some extent, give the advantage that the industry can cope fairly well with a fluctuating demand in the short term, if the demand fluctuations become too large or occur too quickly the construction market as a whole becomes very unstable and prices become erratic and difficult to predict. We have already seen that the industry reacts comparatively slowly to conditions of falling demand, and if demand falls relatively quickly there may be a considerable period of lower than expected tender prices as the same number of firms compete increasingly more fiercely for the available work. Construction, as we have also already seen, tends to be a highly fragmented and specialised business, and firms cannot easily switch their resources to operate in other markets. They will therefore tend only to leave the industry as a last resort; that is, they will tend to try to hang on for as long as possible, usually by progressively reducing the profit margins included in new tenders while at the same time attempting to reduce direct costs to a minimum, often by shedding staff, in the hope that things will improve. If demand continues to fall, or even remains static at low levels, then eventually the market mechanism will come into play and the less competitive, least efficient firms will be forced to leave the industry. This phase will generally occur some considerable time (certainly some months, and perhaps even years) after the initial fall in market demand began.

The effect of this is that, for a period, the industry's production capacity is likely to grossly exceed the amount of work available, and, in the case of a severe fall in demand, the reluctance of individual firms to leave the market, except as a last resort, may mean that a substantial number of firms eventually all leave the industry at the same time. A substantial proportion of the site workforce will attempt to move to other industries. The eventual collapse of the industry, when it does eventually come, may therefore appear to be both sudden and dramatic.

On the other hand, however, if demand begins to rise relatively quickly from some stable level, the reverse applies. Since construction is a business requiring specialised technical knowledge and skills, it is not easy for new firms to enter the market quickly. In addition, it is not easy to expand the pool of skilled labour required rapidly, particularly if many skilled workers have established themselves in other industries. As demand rises, therefore, two things tend to happen:

1. Because construction is a long-term activity, existing firms will be reluctant to expand and new firms will be reluctant to enter the industry until they can be fairly sure that the increase in demand will be sustained for a reasonable period of time. The capacity of the existing firms is exceeded and the tender prices and profit levels of those firms already in the industry will tend to rise. The industry might expect to experience a substantial period of higher than expected tender prices. In addition, because firms can afford to be more selective about the kind of work they are prepared to take on, the rise in tender prices for particularly complex or difficult projects may be even higher than the average for the market as a whole. At the extreme case there is a danger of local construction markets moving towards a situation where the number of contractors is comparatively small in comparison with the number of projects on offer, with the consequent dangers of price fixing, collusion on tender prices etc.

2. Large numbers of relatively unskilled or semi-skilled workers are re-cruited into the industry to cope with the increased demand. Quality standards and industrial productivity tend to fall.

Eventually, of course, the market mechanism will again operate: more firms will enter the industry and/or the capacity of existing firms will be deliberately expanded and the *status quo* will again be restored. Note, however, that, in the case of major fluctuations in demand, a substantial period of stable demand levels may be required before the *status quo* can be restored, the supply and demand sides of the industry will again be in balance, and the market price for construction work will again become reasonably predictable.

It can therefore be seen that, if the construction industry is to remain healthy, there is a need for the average demand for construction work to be at least reasonably predictable and hopefully relatively constant. We have clearly seen that major fluctuations of demand within a comparatively short time-scale or extended periods of demand uncertainty may give rise to serious problems in matching demand and supply and thus in predicting the market price for construction work.

Given the above it would seem that some method of predicting the possible future fluctuations in demand for construction work might be a useful tool for contractors to use in their forward planning. Most analyses of this type are based on some type of historical projection, supplemented by some form of subjective 'expert' judgement, but Oshabajo and Fellows (1991) have shown that it is possible to take advantage of the fact that changes in construction demand generally lag behind the fluctuations in other key economic indicators, principally, it seems, changes in interest rates. They go on to formulate a mathematical model which, they claim, is appropriate for short-term forecasts of between three and four quarters.

1.5   SOURCES OF CONSTRUCTION WORK

Traditionally, most construction work has been let by competitive tender. The process is therefore controlled to a large extent by the industry's clients, the market customers, who invite contractors to tender in competition with each other. On the other hand, the service providers, the sellers in the market-place, take a generally passive role in that they normally have to wait for customers to come to them. While it is, of course, possible for them to improve their chances of being asked (i.e. being included on tender lists) by various forms of advertising (although recent research by Preece (1994) appears to show that few firms do even this effectively), the traditional contracting market is largely demand-led and the conventional commercial practices of attempting to increase sales through advertising and promotion generally do not have the same effect as is the case in industries like manufacturing.

Contractors have attempted to overcome this problem in a number of ways:

1. The growth of property-owning democracies in the developed world has encouraged speculative housing for sale on the open market. This aspect of construction is the closest the construction industry gets to producing consumer goods, and in this sector of the market many of the basic rules of economics which apply to manufacturing industry do apply. Other speculative developments may include offices, industrial parks etc., but involvement in speculative development is a two-edged sword. On the one hand, contractors may be able to use their own speculative building ventures to even out their demand for contract work, but on the other hand the contractor or its partners must finance the whole cost of the development, including the land purchase, from inception until the first units are let or sold. The cash flow for this type of project therefore may be far less predictable than that for a project won in competition, where the employer will usually pay for work completed on a monthly basis. The process can also be risky, since success depends upon the contractor gambling that the property market will continue to rise and that there will be a market for the product at an acceptable price when the work is completed. While the long-term trend is undoubtedly upward, in the short term the property market can be very fickle, particularly in times of recession.

2. Most contractors will attempt to cultivate a number of regular clients who are likely to provide them with a regular programme of work on a negotiated basis. In these cases the contractor will typically attempt to differentiate its service from others available in the market-place on the basis of observable criteria, such as reliability, quality of workmanship, speed of construction or rapidity of response, as well as price, and once such clients have been secured the contractor will usually be prepared to work very hard to keep them. Such arrangements are often in the area of routine maintenance or repair, but may also include new works, although they will not generally be major projects.

3. Some contractors have attempted to improve their market share by providing a system of 'single point' responsibility for clients, usually through the use of 'design and build'-type packages, often linked to a guaranteed maximum price arrangement, where the contractor takes full responsibility for both the design and construction of the works. In the past these packages have tended to be generally limited to fairly simple types of building, but the technique is now beginning to be widely used for a number of complex building types. Macniel (1992), for example, describes the development of a £32 million design and build scheme for a major hospital in Scotland. Some commentators (for example Fellows and Lang-

ford (1993) and Yates (1994)), predict that an increasing volume of construction work worldwide will be procured through this route in the future.

4. Some contractors have attempted to create their own construction market, usually as part of a larger consortium. The basis of these schemes is that projects are identified which would normally be considered as public works, and where a worthwhile income is likely to arise, but where the government or other authority involved does not have the resources to carry them out. Typical examples might be highway works, such as roads, bridges or tunnels, which can be operated on a toll basis, or more complex facilities such as power stations, where the power generated can be sold to an existing power supply authority. The projects are designed and constructed by the consortium, using private capital, and in return the consortium is given a concession to operate the utility for some future period. At the end of the concession period possession of the utility is transferred to the relevant public authority. Projects of this type are known by a number of acronyms, generally variants of build/operate/transfer (BOT), and are becoming very popular. Examples of recently completed successful BOT projects include the Channel Tunnel between Britain and France and the Dartford bridge, while the Hong Kong Cross Harbour Tunnel and the Shajiao 'B' power station in southern China represent examples of successful BOTs which have almost reached the end of their concession periods. Although the concept might appear to be new, Walker (1993) reports that the first true BOT project was probably the Suez Canal. The potential returns to the consortium may be high but the risks may be great.

1.6   THE THEORY OF THE FIRM

Conventional economic theory tells us that all firms will attempt to keep costs and income in equilibrium by assessing likely demand for their product together with the market price for the goods produced, and gearing supply capacity to suit. It might therefore be helpful to look at how well this theory applies to the construction industry.

All firms, including construction firms, have some fixed costs, which they have to pay whether or not they produce anything at all, and some variable costs, which are directly related to the volume of output. In construction, the amount of fixed costs varies according to the nature of the firm. In the case of a general contractor, which relies on subcontracting most of its work, fixed costs may be relatively low, perhaps only comprising office rental, staff salaries, provision of company cars and the cost of financing any working capital. On the other hand, an excavation and earthworks contractor, for example, might have a large amount of capital tied up in expensive plant, with an associated plant yard, workshops etc.

The problem with fixed costs is that they tend to rise in steps. A certain level of fixed cost might be adequate for a certain range of production capacity, and when the end point of the range is reached a further increase in capacity will require that fixed costs increase by a larger amount than a marginal increase in production would justify. The revised level of fixed costs then applies for the next range of production, and so on. Fixed costs may also be difficult to adjust quickly, and changes in fixed costs therefore tend to be considered only in the medium to long term. This means that if we plot the short-term costs of a firm against production capacity, we find that the curve is U-shaped, with the bottom of the U representing the optimum production level, where the cost per unit of production is at its lowest. Cost per unit of production at low levels of production tends to be high, falls to a minimum at some optimum production capacity, and tends to rise again where production approaches the high end of the range.

It is therefore obvious that to maximise profits for a given product price level the firm needs to operate as closely as possible to the optimum unit cost. This is very difficult to do in the construction market, where demand is potentially so unpredictable, but the short-run cost curve will be unique for each firm, and in theory at least it is important that all firms know what their cost per unit of output actually is. An example of the calculation of short-run cost curves is given in Hillebrandt (1985).

Each company will have its own short-run cost curve, which will indicate what the total value of production ought to be for maximum profitability. At any instant in time, therefore, each firm will be in a different trading position, but all firms ought to be attempting to maintain their production at the optimum. What then ought to be the effect of this on tender prices?

For firms operating towards the left-hand end of the curve, i.e. with production levels below the optimum, costs per unit of production are high. In the short run they must attempt to increase production in order to drive costs per unit down; in a construction tendering situation that would mean submitting lower prices and thus hopefully winning more work, but the price must never fall below the firm's minimum cost level. If the minimum cost at which the firm can tender is still above the market price (i.e. if it is still not successful in obtaining work) then it must attempt to reduce fixed costs in order to move its optimum level of production closer to what it can realistically achieve.

Firms operating towards the right-hand end of the short-run curve, however, ought only to tender at a rate which represents a true reflection of their unit costs. Such costs will normally be higher than the market rate, since they will usually be tendering against firms operating at or below optimum capacity. It is therefore less likely that they will be successful, but if they are successful then they will have secured the work at a price which allows them to cover their true costs. If they do get the work then they may gain valuable intelligence about the state of the competition, and this may help them to decide whether or not they should plan for expansion and an increase in fixed costs in the long run.

But how do firms know when they are operating at optimum efficiency? The classical theoretical economics answer is usually thought to be given by the use of marginal analysis techniques. Marginal analysis compares the increase in revenue generated from the last small rise in output (the marginal revenue) with the relevant costs of production (the marginal cost). Normally, of course, for a firm in a healthy trading situation marginal revenue will exceed marginal cost, but the difference between the two will tend to decrease as the firm approaches the limit of its fixed resources. As soon as marginal cost exceeds marginal revenue the firm is no longer efficient, and the firm is therefore operating at maximum efficiency (i.e. the fixed resources of the firm are being used to their maximum) when marginal cost and marginal revenue are equal.

This technique works well in manufacturing industry, where output volume can be fairly closely monitored, controlled and varied in the short term, but it has been pointed out by several commentators (for example Rutter (1993)) that construction does not work like that. Construction projects are generally large, generally indivisible, and generally will each individually comprise a high proportion of the firm's turnover, so the concept of marginal analysis as a precision decision analysis tool in deciding whether or not to tender for new work does not operate very well. The difficulties involved in applying the techniques developed for use in manufacturing engineering to the construction industry have caused many firms simply to ignore economic analysis altogether, but this risks throwing away the potential benefits as well. Standard economics techniques, such as marginal analysis, can give an idea of the firm's efficiency, but the nature of the construction business means that it is very difficult to use such techniques with any great degree of precision.

1.7   REFERENCES

Adrian J.J.A. (1982) *Construction Estimating: An Accounting and Productivity Approach*, Reston Publishing Company, Reston, Virginia.

Briscoe G. (1988) *The Economics of the Construction Industry*, Mitchell, London.

Fellows R. and Langford D. (1993) *Marketing and the Construction Client*, Chartered Institute of Building, London.

Fine B. (1987) 'Kitchen sink economics and the construction industry', in Building, Cost Modelling and Computers (ed. Brandon P.S.), E. & F.N. Spon, London.

Hillebrandt P.M. (1984) *Analysis of the British Construction Industry*, Macmillan, London.

Hillebrandt P.M. (1985) *Economic Theory and the Construction Industry*, 2nd edn, Macmillan, London.

Macniel J. (1992) 'An aesthetic treat', *Building*, 14 August 1992.

Oshabajo A.O. and Fellows R.F. (1991) 'Investigation of leading indicators for the prediction of UK contractor's workloads (total new orders)', in *Management, Quality and Economics in Building*, (eds. Bezalga A. and Brandon P.), E. & F.N. Spon, London.

Park W.R. (1979) *Construction Bidding for Profit*, Wiley, New York.

Powell C.G. (1980) *An Economic History of the British Construction Industry*, Architectural Press, London.

Preece C. (1994) 'Promoting construction for competitive advantage', *Chartered Builder*, July/August 1994, pp. 7–9, Chartered Institute of Building, London.

Rutter G. (1993) *Construction economics: is there such a thing?*, Construction paper No. 18, Chartered Institute of Building, London.

Walker C.T. (1993) 'BOT Infrastructure: Anatomy of Success', *MSc Dissertation*, City Polytechnic of Hong Kong.

Yates J.K. (1994) 'Construction competition and competitive strategies', *Journal of Management in Engineering*, Vol. 10, No. 1, American Society of Civil Engineers.

2   The Estimating Process

2.1   THE PLACE OF ESTIMATING IN THE COMPETITIVE TENDERING PROCESS

The traditional methods of construction procurement in most parts of the world all generally involve some form of competition between a number of contractors, with price usually playing a major part in the selection of the contractor eventually chosen to carry out the work. Contractors therefore need some reliable method of forecasting prices, and therefore likely costs, for future construction work.

Historically, in the competitive tendering situation, the price forecasting technique most commonly used has closely followed that used in industries such as manufacturing engineering. The process is essentially a linear one, in which the contractor first calculates the cost of all of the inputs to the project (i.e. the total cost of the labour, materials, plant, subcontract work etc. required to complete the project; in economic jargon the 'factors of production'), and to this total is added some figure to cover overheads and profit, often in the form of a percentage, to give the price which will be quoted to the client. The total cost of the inputs to the process is usually termed the *estimate*, and the price quoted to the client is usually termed the *tender*. The preparation of the estimate is therefore seen as a mainly technical and factual operation (CIOB (1983), for example, defines estimating as 'the technical process of predicting costs of construction'), and is usually carried out by a specialist estimator.

The tender, on the other hand, represents 'The sum of money, time and other conditions required by the tenderers to carry out the work' (CIOB, 1983). The tendering process must therefore take into account the contractor's assessment of prevailing market conditions, in other words an assessment of what price the market will bear, and the calculation of the tender figure has therefore been seen as a largely subjective commercial management decision. It has conventionally been assumed that the tender will be based on the estimate. CIOB (1983, p. 3), for example, defines tendering as a '...separate and subsequent commercial function based upon the estimate'. The process of converting an estimate into a tender is usually termed *adjudication*.

14

Some commentators, for example Fine (1975) and Ostwald (1992), point out that the validity of the above approach is sometimes questioned on the basis that, in a free market, the link between cost and market price for any goods is at best a tenuous one. The same point is reinforced by Ashworth and Skitmore who, reporting previous research, comment that:

> As a consequence of the theoretical considerations and observed behaviour of contractors in a competitive environment it is not surprising to find references to prices being unrelated to performance or costs of construction.

One example of this phenomenon which is often quoted in construction is that of speculative housing, where the selling price of the product is governed strongly by market demand, and where the price the prospective purchasers are willing (or able) to pay may often bear little or no relationship to the actual costs incurred by the builder. It is held by some that, by extension, the same argument should apply to other sectors of the construction market. If, for example, a hotel chain wishes to build a new hotel, its commercial assessment of the viability of the scheme must include a maximum figure for construction costs beyond which the project would not be commercially feasible. It is therefore this figure which represents the maximum market price which it would be willing to pay for the construction work, and consequently the figure which the lowest tenderer should be aiming to predict.

The difference in practical terms, of course, between the two examples quoted above, is that houses, both new and old, are a commodity which is widely traded on an open market. The market price of new houses – their value to prospective purchasers – is therefore relatively easy for the contractor to assess, and it can then pitch its selling price according to the market value of similar units. In the case of bespoke construction works, such as the construction of a new hotel, however, the market is much less open and the true market value for any particular project is much more difficult to determine. In this case the only person who knows the real commercial value of the construction project is the hotel developer. In the case of a competition based solely on price, therefore, the hotel developer is effectively offering to auction the opportunity to construct the project to the lowest bidder. An excellent discussion of the economic concepts of cost, price and value and the relationship between them is given in Raftery (1991, Ch. 2).

The issue of consideration of the market price will be discussed in more detail in a later chapter, but it is evident that, however the market price is determined, construction companies tendering for work still need to know what their own direct costs for the project will be, if only to give their own 'bottom line' below which it would not be economic for them to carry out the work. The process of estimating is therefore of fundamental importance.

2.2   THE PROCESS OF ESTIMATING

It can clearly be seen from the above that the ability to estimate the likely cost of proposed future construction work reliably is a fundamental requirement for any construction contractor. The estimator's prediction of likely cost will, at the very least, form an important part of the information available to management when establishing the tender price. In addition, if the tender is successful and the contractor is to obtain the anticipated financial return, then the estimate must also effectively become the contractor's budget for construction of the works, and must also provide the basis for the contractor's post-contract costing and valuation systems. It is therefore obvious that every estimate must be compiled in a systematic way, and the information upon which it is based should be as factual as possible. The most variable items are likely to be factors such as production rates, materials wastage etc., and the most reliable source of data for factors such as these ought to be from recorded company data derived from site feedback or work study exercises. Unfortunately, such data are frequently not available, and estimators are therefore frequently forced to fall back on their own skill and experience. Ashworth and Skitmore report that, in the United Kingdom at least:

> Estimators' standard outputs are contained and secretly guarded in their 'black book'. They are only rarely ever amended or revised…. A major reason given why estimators disassociate themselves from site feedback is due to the poor recording systems employed by contractors and hence a lack of confidence in the data provided.

But we have already seen that the estimate is a forecast of future events. It is subject to considerable uncertainty, and it is perhaps for this reason that estimating, particularly in a competitive tendering situation, is considered by some to be 'more an art than a science' (Adrian, 1982, p.4) Fine (1974) went even further and described estimating as:

> …like witchcraft: it involves people foretelling situations about which they can have little real knowledge

and it is perhaps with this thought in mind that Ashworth and Skitmore comment that:

> Builders' estimating has, in the past, had its own mystique, with the result that certain processes discussed both in the classroom and in the estimator's office are found to have little practical relevance.

Estimating is not therefore the precise technical and analytical process which many theorists would have us believe. Estimating must be, to a large extent, a subjective process, and the estimator can never hope to predict actual costs precisely, but the degree of accuracy sought must at least attempt to satisfy two basic criteria:

1. The sums of money allowed in the estimate must be at least high enough to cover the direct cost of the work.

2. The overall tender figure must be low enough to be competitive.

Ashworth and Skitmore report that most estimators are convinced that they are able to consistently estimate to within ±5%, but that research indicates that this figure may be overly optimistic.

2.3   THE PLACE OF THE ESTIMATOR IN THE CONTRACTOR'S ORGANISATION

From a purely technical point of view the estimator's main function is to attempt to forecast the probable prime cost of construction work with the assistance of the tender documents (bill of quantities, specifications and drawings), while maintaining an awareness of the stipulations and constraints of the Conditions of Contract, and in so doing to predict the probable final cost to the contractor of completing the project. But this simple technical view runs the risk of undervaluing the estimator's contribution to the process as a whole. Ayres (1984, p. 18), for example, sees the estimator's input almost lyrically as a fundamental turning point in the project's progress from dream to reality:

> Any building is a dream until construction is started. The architect has a picture on paper, but it is only a picture until the contractor transforms that picture into a solid, three dimensional structure. The estimator is the one who translates that picture into cold hard dollars. Lines on a drawing or phrases in a specification can be changed for the cost of an eraser, but when an estimator says he will furnish a building for a specific sum of money, it is a final action and the first step in the transformation of a dream into a solid object.

Taking into account the implications for the production stage, if the tender should be successful, of any assumptions made in the estimate, it is obvious that the estimator cannot accomplish this task alone. The process of producing an estimate, particularly on larger projects, cannot be seen as a single operation carried out by one single individual. If estimators are to be effective they must work in close liaison with other personnel, who will in due course be responsible for planning the work, for procuring the necessary plant and materials and for carrying out the work on the site.

A 'team approach', at least during the early stages of project appreciation, including buyer, project planner, construction manager and plant manager, as well as the estimator, will assist in identifying and analysing potential problem areas which might not be apparent to an estimator working in isolation and which, in turn, might not be considered until construction works had commenced on site, at which point it would usually be too late to take corrective action. During the project appreciation stage the team should also consider, evaluate and make decisions about factors such as the proposed construction programme, alternative methods of construction and site layout.

It is sometimes said that the major function of the estimator is to obtain work, and there is sometimes a tendency to blame the estimator if the prices quoted by the contractor are too high. If the firm is short of work, the estimator is frequently told to 'sharpen his pencil'. This is, in the majority of cases, both unfair and counter-productive. The procurement of work is a management responsibility. While it is true that the main reason for preparing the estimate is to help in the procurement of new work, the estimator's function is simply to make a prediction of the probable cost of the work to the contractor, and one of the most important factors must be consistency of approach. Davies (1980) sums up the issue rather well:

> Ensure the estimating team is consistent. Consistency and reliability are the key characteristics needed in estimators. When considering a tender the first essential is to have confidence in the estimated prime cost and be reassured that it has been prepared on a basis consistent with the estimates looked at yesterday, last week and last month, and that this basis produces as accurate a forecast as can reasonably be expected in the face of many uncertainties.

2.4   SKILLS AND TRAINING

In the UK estimating is not generally considered to be a separate profession in its own right, and estimators tend to be drawn from a variety of different backgrounds within the construction industry. There are, in the UK, no formal education or training courses for estimators, and therefore most of their knowledge has to be gained through experience. The situation is, however, different in other parts of the world. In the USA, for example, the American Society of Professional Estimators provides construction industry estimators with a formal professional framework, including a published code of ethics, and also sponsors estimating education through scholarships and participation in a variety of educational programmes.

While a good grounding in construction technology is essential, it is also important that young estimators spend a reasonable period on site observing how things are actually done in order to supplement, and perhaps complement, their theoretical knowledge of how things ought to be done. The following, compiled from a variety of published sources, are generally accepted to be the most important technical skills which a good estimator should possess:

1. The ability to read, quickly understand and summarise both written and graphical technical documentation.

2. Well-developed organisational and communication skills.

3. Good numerical and analytical skills.

4. The ability to visualise the project in three dimensions from two-dimensional drawings.

5. A good grasp of quantity surveying construction measurement skills.

6. A good understanding of labour and equipment performance, and the ability to recognise those unusual situations where the 'standard' allowances no longer apply.

7. A clear understanding of the commonly used Conditions of Contract.

8. Creativity and imagination.

2.5 MANAGEMENT OF THE ESTIMATING AND TENDERING PROCESS – AN OVERVIEW

Management of the estimating and tendering process will usually involve the following activities:

1. Decision to tender

2. Examination of the tender documents

3. Establishment of a programme for estimate and tender preparation

4. Site visit

5. Analysis of prime cost and provisional sums

6. Preparation of outline method statements and production programme

7. Subcontractors' and suppliers' enquiries

8. Estimation of the direct costs

9. Estimate appraisal and adjudication

10. Assembly of the bid documentation and submission of the tender

Some of these stages are essentially management decisions, and are dealt with in detail elsewhere in this book. Specifically, stage 1, the decision to submit a tender, is covered in Chapter 13, and stage 9, estimate appraisal and adjudication, and stage 10, assembly of the bid documentation in are covered in Chapter 11. In addition, stage 6, the preparation of method statements and production programme, is dealt with separately in Chapter 5, and stage 7, subcontractors and suppliers, in Chapter 7.

The remainder of the above activities comprise those management activities usually dealt with by the estimator, and are considered here.

2.6   EXAMINATION OF THE TENDER DOCUMENTS

The tender documents usually comprise a selection of the project drawings, the specification, the Conditions of Contract, and, for larger projects, the bill of quantities. A close examination of the tender documents is essential, first of all to ensure that all of the documents have been received, but secondly to gain a thorough grasp of the work required. It is essential that all staff involved in the estimating process have a thorough understanding of the project if the estimating process is to be successful.

A further reason for a close examination of the tender documents is to gain an impression of the appropriateness of the Conditions of Contract as compared with the completeness of the design. Some Forms of Contract and some Standard Methods of Measurement assume that the design is virtually complete at the time of tender, and the degree of uncertainty and risk faced by the contractor may be considerably increased if this is not the case, especially where a bill of quantities purports to give accurately measured quantities for the work. A more detailed consideration of the risks posed by incomplete design is included in Chapter 12.

When examining the documents, the estimator should also be particularly on the lookout for:

1. Any amendments to the standard Conditions of Contract.

2. Non-standard payment or retention provisions.

3. Project time-scale and any associated liquidated damages requirements.

4. Provision of bid or performance bonds.

5. Unusual insurance requirements.

6. Any discrepancies between the various documents, for example between the drawings and the bill of quantities or between the specification and the drawings.

7. Clear and unambiguous specifications and bill of quantities.

8. Any outstanding information required.

The time available for the estimator to carry out this task is usually very limited, but it is only through this close and detailed scrutiny of the project documentation that estimators and their colleagues will be able to form judgements about possible methods of construction, buildability, likely construction programme and the degree of risk involved in the project.

Once this initial examination is completed, or perhaps sometimes in parallel with it, the estimator needs to identify and abstract from the bills those sections of the work which it is envisaged will be subcontracted, and also to abstract details of all of the major materials required, together with their total quantities.

In addition to a study of the project tender documents, there is a wide variety of 'standard' documents which may apply to the works. Perhaps the most important among these, from the estimator's point of view, are the various standard methods of measurement for construction work in common use, and the various standard forms of contract in use in the industry. Some combination of these standard documents often forms one of the main planks upon which the framework of the project procurement methodology is based, and may be referred to in the tender documentation, but copies will rarely be provided. These documents include important information about the contractor's general obligations and, in the case of Standard Methods of Measurement, about items of work which the estimator will be deemed to have included in his estimate, but which will not be explicitly quantified in the bill of quantities. It is therefore most important that the estimator should be thoroughly familiar with their scope and contents.

2.7   ESTABLISHMENT OF A PROGRAMME FOR ESTIMATE AND TENDER PREPARATION

The estimator will usually act as the manager of the estimate production process, and will be responsible for coordinating the work of colleagues. The estimator will therefore be responsible for establishing the necessary key dates to allow the estimate to be prepared within the time available. It is perhaps worth noting that the time allowed for preparation of a typical tender for a project based on a bill of quantities is usually a maximum of only four or five weeks, and this crucial activity will typically represent perhaps only a small proportion, perhaps one thirtieth or less, of the overall project time-scale.

The following dates must be clearly established as early as possible:

1. Latest date for dispatch of enquiries for materials, plant and subcontractors' work

2. Latest date for receipt of quotations

3. Finalisation of the method statement

4. Completion of pricing

5. Adjudication meeting

6. Tender submission

2.8 SITE VISIT

For most projects a site visit will be essential in order to gain an accurate impression of the site and its surroundings. Among the more important considerations should be:

1. General site particulars, including soil and groundwater, location and topography, any existing structures, condition and present use of any buildings abutting the site, availability of drainage and other public utility services, areas available for materials storage, site hutting etc., site access, police regulations and parking restrictions, security and likelihood of theft and vandalism, and trees to be protected.

2. Location of the nearest town, travelling distance, public transport links, possible accommodation for workforce etc.

3. Location of suitable tips, charges.

4. Demolition works and possible salvageable materials.

5. Local labour, subcontractors and materials suppliers.

6. Possibility of complaints regarding noise, dust and other pollution.

7. Weather conditions.

Photographs should be taken of the site, showing access, relevant buildings and other structures, and any other important features. The use of a standard pro forma such as that given in CIOB (1983) may be a useful way to ensure that all the relevant detail is collected.

2.9 ANALYSIS OF PRIME COST AND PROVISIONAL SUMS

Provisional sums are sums of money included to cover work which, at the time the tender documents are prepared, cannot be adequately described and measured. In the case of a bill of quantities measured in accordance with the *Standard Method of Measurement for Building Works*, 7th edn (SMM7) in the UK, provisional sums must be identified as being for either 'defined' or 'undefined' work. 'Undefined' work is work which may or may not be required, whereas 'defined' work is work which is known to be required, but which cannot be adequately measured and described at the time the bills are prepared. One important point arising from this is that preliminaries and overheads costs included in the tender must cover defined work, but do not have to cover undefined work.

Prime cost sums are sums of money inserted into project documentation to cover work to be completed by subcontractors and suppliers who will be chosen by the architect or engineer to complete certain specified parcels of work.

Relevant issues to do with the pricing of work in connection with prime cost sums are considered in detail in Chapter 7, but an early analysis of the approximate total proportion of the project value covered by prime cost and provisional sums will be useful to the estimator in gaining a 'feel' for the project as a whole.

2.10 REFERENCES

Adrian J.J.A. (1982) *Construction Estimating*, Reston Publishing Co, Reston VA.

Ashworth A., and Skitmore R.M. *Accuracy in Estimating*, Occasional Paper No. 27, Chartered Institute of Building, London.

Ayres C. (1984) *Specifications for architecture, engineering and construction*, second edition, McGraw Hill, USA

CIOB (1983) *Code of Estimating Practice*, The Chartered Institute of Building, London.

Davies F.A.W. (1980) 'Preparation and settlement of competitive lump sum tenders for building works', in *The Practice of Estimating*, The Chartered Institute of Building, London.

Fine B. (1974) 'Tendering Strategy, *Building*, 25 October 1974, pp. 115–21.

Fine B. (1975) 'Tendering Strategy', in *Aspects of the Economics of Construction*, (ed. Turin D.A.), Macmillan, London.

Ostwald P.F. (1992) *Engineering Cost Estimating*, 3rd edn, Prentice-Hall, Englewood Cliffs NJ.

Raftery J. (1991) *Principles of Building Economics*, BSP Professional Books, United Kingdom.

3 Estimating Techniques Using Historical Cost Data

3.1 INTRODUCTION

A wide range of techniques exists for the forecasting of construction costs and prices, ranging from, at one extreme, simple unit cost-based predictions, to complex analytical estimating techniques at the other. The particular technique chosen in each case, and the degree of accuracy of the resulting prediction, will depend to a very large extent on the amount and quality of information about the proposed building which is available at the time.

Research by Fortune and Lees (1994) shows that the majority of early stage cost estimating techniques in current use are still concerned primarily with initial capital cost, despite a growing pressure from academics for a deeper consideration of estimating systems which deal with the whole life cost of projects. The major techniques in common use, in increasing order of potential accuracy, are therefore:

1. Cost per functional unit

2. Cost per unit of floor area

3. Elemental cost estimating

4. Analytical estimating

The first three techniques generally make use of historical data, and are usually used for early stage cost predictions at various stages throughout the design process. While these early stage techniques (or variations of them) have long been used by contractors for smaller projects, usually those based on plans and specifications, they are now beginning to become more widely used for larger projects, particularly with the present shift towards design and build-based approaches to construction procurement, where the design may be incomplete at the time of the bid submission. Nonetheless, use of these techniques, and collection of the necessary data to support them, is more

24

usually considered to be part of the quantity surveyor's construction economics function, and it would perhaps be more usual for contractors to seek advice from specialist quantity surveyors in the preparation of estimates of this type where complex projects are concerned. These historical cost-based techniques are therefore considered here in outline only, and those seeking a more detailed treatment of the subject should refer to a specialised text on construction economics, such as Seeley (1995) or Ferry and Brandon (1991).

The fourth technique, analytical estimating, makes use of current cost data and is the approach most often used by contractors in the competitive tendering situation. Analytical methods are dealt with separately in detail in Chapters 4–6.

3.2 COST PER FUNCTIONAL UNIT

One way of forecasting the probable cost of a proposed new building, perhaps the easiest, would be to look at how much similar buildings have cost in the past. If, for example, a contractor has previously built a school of a certain size and level of specification, and is lucky enough to be invited to build another school of similar size and specification but on a different site, it ought, in the absence of any detailed design information for the new building, to be possible to use the historical cost data from the first scheme to give a reasonably accurate prediction for the construction cost of the new project. The data would of course need to be adjusted for the effects of time (cost inflation) and different site and market conditions, but nevertheless the data should be sufficient to give a reasonably accurate guideline estimate for the cost of the new building.

It is, however, rare to get two schemes that are exactly the same, and if we are to consider the use of historical data of this type we are therefore forced into a position where the best we can hope for is to find one or more previous schemes which are, in some respects, similar to the proposed project, and somehow to adjust the cost data to suit the new scheme.

Perhaps the simplest way is to express the historical costs in terms of some functional unit. In the case of a school, for example, costs could be expressed per pupil place, or in the case of a hospital in terms of cost per bed. Using this very rough and ready analysis the historical costs of a number of previous schemes, each suitably adjusted for time, can be combined and used to prepare early stage cost estimates for the construction of similar buildings in the future. The estimates will, of course, be subject to a large margin of error, perhaps as much as ±30%, but may nevertheless be useful in setting outline budgets.

This, and the other following price forecasting techniques described, are fairly well developed in the case of building projects, but much less so for civil engineering, since the costs for this type of work are considered to be much more dependent upon the detailed programme and working methods to be used. There has consequently been a tendency to postpone any attempt at detailed estimating until the tendering stage, relying up to that point on estimates prepared on a simple 'cost per mile [km]' basis. According to Spon (1994, p. 3):

> The result has been a growing pressure on the part of project sponsors for an improvement in budgetary advice, so that a decision to commit expenditure to a particular project is then taken on firmer grounds. The absence of a detailed pricing method during the pre-contract phase also inhibits the accurate costing of alternative designs and regular cost checking to ensure that the design is being developed within the employer's budget.

3.3   COSTS PER UNIT OF FLOOR AREA

An alternative to the cost per functional unit technique is to convert the costs from a range of buildings to costs per unit of floor area – normally either a cost/m^2 or a cost/sq. ft. If a contractor were to analyse all of the schemes in which it was involved on this basis, it would have a cost data bank which could be used for new projects. The contractor might, for example, given a new hotel to price, be able to say that past experience shows that hotel buildings ought to cost between, say, £1000 and £1200 per square metre. A similar approach can be taken for civil engineering work. It is, for example, common to price bridges at a price per m^2 of deck area, the various different types of road on an overall cost per mile/km, including pavements, footways, drainage, signs, lighting, barriers etc. The costs would of course have to be adjusted to a common time base, and perhaps some adjustment would need to be made for location, but in theory at least, the more previous projects available the more accurate the prediction for the new project ought to be.

In practice this cost per unit area approach is very widely used for early cost appraisal, and given an outline brief which, for example, calls for 3500 m^2 of offices, shops and flats in a mixed development it would be possible to apply some overall cost assessment, say £600 m^2, to give a predicted cost for the project of about £2.1 m. Of course, the estimate cannot be very accurate because there are so many unknowns, and so it is really not a good idea to give single rate estimates of this type. The cost at this stage would be more likely to be given as a range, say ±30% (i.e. £1.5 m–£2.75 m). Nevertheless, it is sometimes unfortunate that the first figure quoted tends to be the one that the client remembers, and thus all too often becomes the cost limit for the project – the cost target against which the architects, engineers and contractors must work – and the project then becomes strongly finance-led.

Note also that floor area for this purpose is defined as the gross floor area measured to the inside of the external walls and measured over internal

Table 3.1 Initial budget

Proposed development, Anytown
Initial outline cost estimate

		£
Shops	500 m^2 × £300 =	0.15 m
Offices	2000 m^2 × £700 =	1.40 m
Flats	1000 m^2 × £400 =	0.40 m
Total estimated cost		£1.95 m

partitions, lift shafts and the like. This method should be distinguished from the floor area calculation used by letting agents, who are concerned with the net floor area that is actually usable. The net floor area may therefore be considerably, perhaps 10–30%, less than the gross floor area as quoted by the quantity surveyor.

In the case of a mixed development, such as that mentioned above (flats, offices and shops), the accuracy of the estimate might be improved as the design develops by using different costs/m^2 for each of the different types of accommodation, as shown in Table 3.1.

Again, the total cost ought to be given as a range to indicate the degree of potential accuracy, perhaps in this case, for example, ±15% (i.e. £1.65 m–£2.25 m).

This cost/m^2 approach using historical cost data from previous contracts is very useful, particularly during the early design stage. It is quick, simple and anyone can understand it, but the level of accuracy tends to be low, owing to the following disadvantages:

1. No two buildings are ever exactly alike.

2. All of the previous costs must be adjusted to a constant time base.

3. Some predictions need to be made about the current market environment and the effect it is likely to have on the new project, but it is also necessary to know what effect market forces had on the projects used as a base.

4. With only a cost/m^2 to work from we have no indication of any problems that might be posed by the site or the design of the new building.

5. The basic cost/m^2 approach makes no allowance for the cost effects of the proposed procurement methodology.

It is also evident that if historical cost information is to be used to attempt to estimate the cost of new, as yet undesigned, projects, then the previous projects need to be analysed in much more detail than simply calculating the cost/m² of floor area.

It is obviously essential to choose as a basis buildings of roughly the same type and standard of specification, but in addition we also need to know, at least:

1. The procurement method and the degree of risk which tendering contractors were being asked to bear.

2. The degree of competition.

3. The project start date and the tender period in order that we can make some adjustment for the time delay.

4. Any abnormal costs attributable to the site.

5. Something about the constructional form and design approach. Since no two buildings are ever exactly alike, it is necessary to develop some mechanism to allow us to compare the costs of apparently different buildings with each other, and for this we need an understanding of the way in which design variables affect project cost.

While a detailed consideration of most of the above factors is considered to be beyond the scope of this text, it might be useful to look briefly at the following two aspects:

1. Methods of relating historical costs from a number of schemes to a common time base.

2. The effects of changes in some simple design variables relating to the building geometry on the project economics.

3.4   UPDATING OF COSTS FROM PREVIOUS SCHEMES TO A COMMON BASE

The most common way to relate the costs of different schemes to a common base is through the use of some type of index. Two types are common:

1. An index measuring changes in building *cost* which attempts to chart changes in the cost of whole buildings by measuring changes in the market prices of the principal raw ingredients (labour, materials, plant costs etc.).

2. An index measuring changes in the level of *tender prices* for construction work.

Both may be useful to contractors, and both have advantages and disadvantages.

3.4.1 An Index of Building Cost

Indices charting the movement of prices of labour and specific raw materials have two primary advantages:

1. They are easy to construct

2. The basic data are readily available and widely published.

The normal method of operation is to select some suitable base date from which to construct the index, and this initial starting point is conventionally given an index number of 100. Subsequent price movements in particular commodities are then measured by comparing the price at any future date with the price at the base date and expressing the result as an index number. The formula for constructing the new index is then:

$$\text{New index} = \frac{\text{New price} \times 100}{\text{Initial price}}$$

So if, as a simple example, we take an index to measure changes in the price of ready mixed concrete:

base date (say January 1980) index 100

price at base date: £21 per m^3

price in January 1994: £41.50 per m^3

Index at January 1994 is therefore £41.50 × 100 / £21 = 197.61

Using this technique it is possible to track the movement of the prices of the individual inputs to the construction process with considerable accuracy, but to be of any real use for total project cost prediction, it is necessary to combine the price movements of all of the individual components into an index to represent the building as a whole. This is not as easy as it may at first sight appear, since the prices for the different resources tend to vary at different rates, and the different inputs have different significance in different buildings depending upon the particular combination of resources used in their construction. For example, the price of concrete would be a very significant factor in a concrete-framed building, while the price of steel might be relatively less significant, but the balance of priorities would be changed significantly in the case of a steel-framed structure.

It is therefore necessary to construct some mechanism to assign a weighting to each of the inputs to the construction process to indicate their relative importance in each individual structure, and this is conventionally done according to the quantity of each resource in any particular project.

Having assigned a weighting to each component resource, the results of the calculations for all of the component resources are then combined in order to arrive at an index number for the project as a whole, as shown in the following formula:

$$\text{Building cost index} = \frac{\displaystyle\sum_{i}^{\text{No. of items}} \frac{\text{Current price}}{\text{Original price}} \times 100 \times \text{Weighting}}{\displaystyle\sum_{i}^{\text{No. of items}} \text{Weighting}}$$

There are a number of potential improvements which could be made to refine this approach, but the above gives a general idea of the basic technique.

As stated above, the main advantage of this technique is that the basic price movement data required for each of the component parts are readily available, and it can therefore give a good indication of overall movements in building prices. The major disadvantage of relying on this technique as a predictor of construction price, however, is that the method is only concerned with measuring variations in the market prices of the inputs to the building process. In any competitive tendering situation, market forces are likely to be a significant factor, and this is not reflected in the index. Although the approach can give a very accurate guide to the movement of contractors' costs, the use of a cost-based index alone as a predictor of construction price is less reliable.

3.4.2   A Tender-based Price Index

The second type of index commonly used is an index which attempts to chart the movement of tender prices. The general technique is to compare prices for selected measured items in tender bills with prices current at some suitable base date which are set out in a comprehensive master schedule. The cumulative variation in price between the project in question and the base schedule is then expressed as an index.

Obviously, the ideal would be to compare all of the prices for the whole project with the rates in the base schedule, but in practice this would be extremely time-consuming. Research has shown that, in a typical building project, a large proportion of the total cost, often as much as 80%, is covered in a small proportion, often as low as 20%, of the measured items. It is therefore possible to achieve acceptable standards of accuracy by using a sampling process from the items in the project bills, and research originally done some 20 years ago by the Directorate of Quantity Surveying Services based in the UK Department of the Environment has shown that in practice a sample of the most significant items in each trade up to a total of 25% of the trade cost is sufficient to give an acceptably accurate indication of the pricing level. This sample of items is then re-priced using rates from the base schedule, and by comparing base prices with tender prices an index number is derived.

Obviously, if the index numbers obtained are to be used to attempt to predict future changes in tender prices the greater the number of projects that can be analysed the better. In the UK, the Royal Institution of Chartered Surveyors Building Cost Information Service claims that a sample of about 80 projects is required in each quarter to give statistically reliable data. It is highly unlikely that the average contractor will have this volume of information available every quarter, and therefore the results obtained must be treated with some caution, but over time the technique can give a reasonable indication of trends in the movement of tender prices.

We can therefore see that a tender-based price index of this type has considerable advantages over a cost-based index in that:

1. It measures the change in the price of construction work to the client taking into account the market forces which affect the tendering process.

2. It is easy to operate once the base schedule has been prepared and it is ideally suited to computer operation

3. It is largely independent of building type and function and allows tender price trends for dissimilar buildings to be compared.

3.4.3 Application of Indices in Cost Estimating

Once the relevant historical indices have been calculated we can use them to update historical scheme costs to a common base using the formula:

$$\text{Percentage variation} = \frac{(\text{Current index} - \text{Original index}) \times 100}{\text{Original index}}$$

The process is illustrated in the following simple example:

Date of tender of existing project: March 1990

Proposed date of tender for new project: December 1993

Tender price index March 1990 = 705

Tender price index December 1993 = 770

Percentage increase to be applied March 1990–December 1993:

$$\frac{(770 - 705) \times 100}{705} = 9.22\%$$

Statistical techniques can also be used to project trends from the historical data to give predictions of future cost and price increases.

3.5   EFFECT OF BUILDING GEOMETRY ON PROJECT COST

Let us now consider the effect of some basic design decisions relating to the geometry of a proposed building on the likely project cost. While much of the building geometry will be dictated by the constraints and orientation of the site, it is still worthwhile considering, in outline at least, the effects of factors such as building shape, scale, storey height and overall building height on the economics of the project.

3.5.1   Plan Shape

Consider the various building plan shapes shown in Figure 3.1. The height of each building is 3.00 m, and the total floor area provided by each shape is 400 m^2, but the areas of external wall required to enclose the various buildings are as follows:

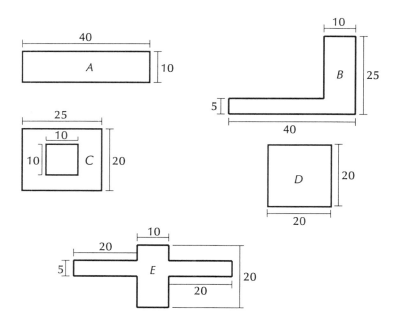

Figure 3.1   Economics of plan shape.

Building A = 300 m²

Building B = 390 m²

Building C = 390 m²

Building D = 240 m²

Building E = 420 m²

All of the shapes enclose the same area, but plainly the quantities of enclosing wall differ considerably. Shape D requires the least area (240 m²), whereas E requires the most (420 m²; an increase of almost 70%), while the others fall somewhere in-between.

It is therefore obvious that simply to use a cost/m² of floor area rate for a new building, even if the area were still to be 400 m², without considering plan shape could potentially be very inaccurate. Historical costs/m² of floor area alone are thus seen to be a very blunt instrument indeed, and we therefore need some additional mechanism to describe the geometry of the building. There have been a number of attempts to develop mathematical formulae to model the cost efficiency of various building shapes, and several alternative methods are listed in Ferry and Brandon (1991, pp. 199–200). One very simple and popular approach at the early design stage is to use ratios such as, for example, the ratio of external wall area/floor area to represent the envelope shape, and the ratio of internal partition area/floor area to represent the extent of internal subdivision.

Using this approach the wall/floor ratios for the buildings shown in Figure 3.1 are:

Building A = 0.75

Building B = 0.975

Building C = 0.975

Building D = 0.6

Building E = 1.05

For building D, therefore only 0.6 m² of external wall is required to enclose each 1 m² of floor area, whereas for building E the quantity of external wall required for each 1 m² of floor area is 1.05 m². It is therefore obvious that the lower the wall/floor ratio the more economical the proposed building will be, at least in terms of its external envelope. Similar techniques, using a partition/floor ratio, can be applied in evaluating the extent of internal subdivision.

3.5.2   Effects of Scale (Size)

Having demonstrated the effect on the wall/floor ratio of changing the basic plan shape, it is obvious that the ratio will also change if the vertical height is changed. But the wall/floor ratio is also affected by changes in scale.

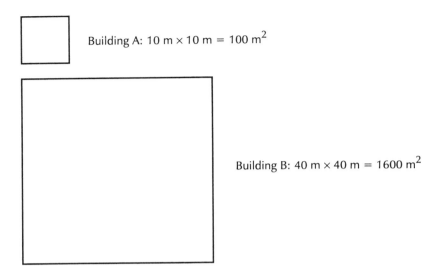

Figure 3.2   Effect of scale.

Compare the two buildings shown in Figure 3.2. In this case both buildings are square, and so should show the same degree of economy in terms of basic shape. Both buildings are also 4 m high. In the case of building A the wall to floor ratio is 1.60, but in the case of building B the wall to floor ratio is only 0.4. Building A therefore requires 1.6 m^2 of external wall for every 1 m^2 of floor area, whereas building B only requires 0.4 m^2 of external wall for each 1 m^2 of floor area. It is therefore apparent that scale (size), as well as plan shape, affects the economics of the building.

3.5.3   Storey Heights

Using a basic cost/m^2 of floor area takes no account of the storey height, and changes in the storey height of buildings of a constant floor area will obviously give rise to changes in the wall/floor and partition/floor ratios and thus to changes in the overall building cost.

Changes in storey height will also affect other vertical elements, such as services, staircases and structural frame.

3.5.4   Building Height

High-rise buildings are almost always more expensive to build than low-rise ones. Seeley (1995) reports a Department of the Environment study in the UK which showed the costs of local authority office blocks '...rising fairly uniformly by about two per cent per floor when increasing the height above four storeys'. The basic reasons for this are:

1. High-rise structural forms are generally more expensive than low-rise, and may also require special foundation solutions

2. Building services in tall buildings usually require special consideration; for example, it may be necessary to install pumps for the water systems, high-speed lifts, special fire protection systems etc.

3. The necessity to provide dedicated building services and/or fire refuge floors at intervals of, say, every 10–15 floors.

4. Construction of high-rise buildings will usually demand specialised construction equipment, and construction costs will generally be more expensive than for a low-rise solution.

On the other hand, however, these effects may be offset by the need to make the maximum use of highly priced land, and the increased costs of high-rise solutions may be completely negated in the context of the overall development equation.

3.6   IMPROVING THE ACCURACY OF THE DATA

The accuracy of the cost prediction can be improved, particularly in respect of the vertical elements like walls, but also for elements like roofs and foundations, which on multi-storey buildings are shared between a number of floors, if one calculates the cost/m^2 of the actual components themselves rather than the cost of the whole building per m^2 of floor area. We could therefore, for example, express the cost of foundations/m^2 of ground floor area, the roof as a cost/m^2 of roof area, the external walls as a cost per m^2 of external wall area and so on.

The rates and quantities derived in this way are known as element unit rates (EUR) and element unit quantities (EUQ) respectively. It is, however, self-evident that derivation of this level of information requires a much more detailed analysis of previous projects to identify the costs and areas for each functional element of the building. A comprehensive library of historical cost information, in the form of detailed cost analyses, is therefore a very important quantity surveying resource. In the UK, the Royal Institution of Chartered Surveyors Building Cost Information Service publishes a detailed guide for the preparation of cost analyses to an established standard (BCIS, 1969), and also provides a forum within which subscribing members can submit cost analyses for their own projects for inclusion in a central computer database, the whole of which is then available for all subscribing members to access.

3.7   ELEMENTAL COST ESTIMATING

Elemental cost estimating is sometimes used by contractors in the preparation of tenders for work procured on a design and build basis, where the estimation of likely cost must be carried out in parallel with the development of the design.

The elemental cost estimating and monitoring process is therefore usually considered to be an ongoing activity which continues in parallel with the design process, with the objective of monitoring, evaluating and progressively refining the probable cost of the work throughout the design stage, hopefully to a progressively greater level of detail and accuracy. The process is therefore one of attempting to cost the evolving design, but even at initial feasibility study stage, where information is still extremely limited and very sketchy, the above ideas can still be used to improve the level of accuracy of the estimate.

Consider, for example, a hypothetical proposed development comprising an eight-storey office building with a total floor area of 7200 m^2 and a ground floor area of 900 m^2. The architect has indicated that the building will be rectangular on plan, with a span of about 15 m. In this case, therefore, the length of the building will be 60 m (900 m^2/15 m), and the perimeter of the external walls will therefore be 150 m. Assuming a floor/floor height of, say, 3.30 m, the total external wall area will therefore be 3960 m^2, and the external wall/floor ratio will therefore be 0.55 (3960 m^2/7200 m^2).

The approximate elemental breakdown of the cost of the proposed building at this early design stage might therefore be calculated as shown in Table 3.2.

The use of appropriate computer techniques can be very helpful in permitting alternative design options to be quickly modelled and evaluated, and they may also provide facilities for some sensitivity testing of the model. At the very lowest level, a simple spreadsheet program can be extremely useful. The use of computers in the estimating process is considered in more detail later.

The use of an elemental approach at this early stage obviously still involves a considerable number of assumptions, but the elemental cost plan will be progressively refined and expanded as the design progresses to reflect the actual design decisions made by the design team. As the design evolves and more detailed information becomes available, the major cost-significant items of work are measured using approximate quantities techniques, and the costs are refined to reflect the actual work required. As this process continues current prices may be used to replace the historical data, thus improving the accuracy of the estimate still further.

Table 3.2 Example preliminary cost estimate

Proposed 7200 m² eight storey office building
Preliminary cost appraisal

Element specification	Quantity factor (QF)	EUR (£)	Cost/m² of floor area
Foundations (spread over 8 floors so QF = 1/8 = 0.125	0.125	210	26.25
Structural frame (including stairs	1.00	100	100.00
Roof (assume concrete slab & asphalt spread over 8 floors)	0.125	75	9.38
External walls (assume curtain walling)	0.55	300	165.00
Internal partitions	0.35	50	17.50
Finishes and fittings (assume medium quality)	1.00	60	60.00
Services			
plumbing	1.00	15	15.00
air conditioning	1.00	160	160.00
electricity	1.00	65	65.00
fire fighting	1.00	5	5.00
lifts (assume 4 × £45 000 = £180 000/7200 m² = £25/m²)	1.00	25	25.00
External works say 5%			648.13
			32.41
Preliminaries say 10%			680.54
			68.05
Contingencies and design risk say 7.5%			740.59
Total budget cost/m²			796.13

Total project estimated cost 7200 m² × £796.13/m² = say £5.75 m

3.8   CONTINGENCY ALLOWANCES

It is normal practice in any estimate to make some allowance to cover the extent of the perceived risk inherent both in the project and in the estimating process, and this allowance is sometimes termed the contingency sum. In the past, allowances of this type have often been simply an educated guess, or at best have been estimated in a fairly unsystematic way on the basis of the estimator's past experience. It has subsequently been shown that, when operating in this way, estimators are more likely to underestimate than overestimate the sums required, and contemporary developments in risk analysis techniques now mean that risks can be quantified with much more accuracy.

Barnes (1989) argues that it is no longer acceptable for contingency allowances to be subjectively assessed on the basis of educated guesswork. Instead, he proposes that the risks implicit in the estimate should be assessed and quantified through the use of Monte Carlo simulations to provide a risk profile of the project from which contingency allowances can then be derived with some degree of objectivity.

3.9   ACCURACY OF EARLY COST FORECASTS

Provided that the original assumptions were reasonably accurate, and provided that the development of the design does not result in the cost allocated for each of the elements in the cost plan being exceeded, the forecast given by the above techniques should be an acceptably accurate estimate of project cost for contractors to use as a basis for design and build tenders, where the design may be significantly incomplete, at least in detail, at the time of bid submission.

There has been considerable research into both the accuracy of quantity surveyors' early forecasts of construction cost and also into the factors which influence accuracy, spread over the past 30 years, but the main effort in this field has been concentrated in the past decade or so. Skitmore *et al.* (1990) present a good review of the current literature, and state that they have found that the results of previous studies were in many cases contradictory and widely different. As regards the accuracy of early stage cost predictions, the overall mean seems to be around ±15% at early design stage, reducing to ±8% or so at tender stage, but the coefficient of variation is very large.

According to Skitmore, however, attempts to forecast final cost, particularly for schemes which display a high level of technical innovation, are fraught with peril. Examples quoted include the Humber Bridge (estimate £19 m, final cost £120 m) and the National Westminster Tower (initial estimate £15 m, final cost £115 m), both in the UK, and the Sydney Opera House (estimate £2.5 m, final cost £87 m) in Australia. These are, of course, exceptional cases, but they do serve to illustrate the point that early estimation of construction cost is an art as much as a science. Any early estimates of cost should therefore be regarded as indicators of an order of cost rather than a firm and precise statement.

As far as civil engineering work is concerned, Barnes (1989) quotes figures of ±33% at feasibility stage, while Thompson (1989), reporting on earlier research, says '...the average increase in value [between pre-contract estimate and tender] of civil engineering contracts utilising bills of quantities has been shown to be 10.5%'.

3.10 REFERENCES

Barnes N.M.L. (1989) 'Financial Control of Construction', in *Control of Engineering Projects* (ed. Wearne S.), Thomas Telford, London.

BCIS (1969) *Standard Form of Cost Analysis: Principles, Instructions and Definitions*, The Royal Institution of Chartered Surveyors, London.

Ferry D.J. and Brandon P.S. (1991) *Cost Planning of Buildings*, 6th edn, BSP Professional Books, UK.

Fortune C. and Lees M. (1994) 'Early cost advice for clients', *Chartered Surveyor Monthly*, March 1994 pp. 18–19, Royal Institution of Chartered Surveyors, London.

Seeley I.H. (1995) *Building Economics*, 4th edn, Macmillan, Basingstoke.

Skitmore M., Stradling S., Touhy A. and Mkwezalamba H. (1990) *Accuracy of Construction Price Forecasts*, University of Salford, UK.

Spon (1994) *Spon's Civil Engineering and Highway Works Price Book*, 8th edn (1994), E. & F.N. Spon, London.

Thompson P.A. (1989) 'Financial Control of Public Works', in *Control of Engineering Projects* (ed. Wearne S.), Thomas Telford, London.

4 Unit Rate Estimating

4.1 INTRODUCTION

The estimating and cost forecasting techniques previously considered have relied mainly on the use of historical cost data to attempt to predict likely costs at an early stage of design. As the design develops, however, contractors will usually try, as far as possible, to use analytical estimating methods using current cost data as a base.

Two major analytical techniques are in common use. *Unit rate estimating* uses predetermined output rates for labour and plant, in conjunction with a price per unit for materials, to calculate a rate per unit (m, m^2, m^3, nr etc.) for some measured item of work, and this unit rate is then set against a total measured quantity. *Operational estimating*, on the other hand, aims to calculate the total cost for a complete work package by determining the total amount of material required together with the overall length of time that the required labour and plant resources are needed on the site for completion of the whole operation. The total operational cost may then need to be broken down into individual unit rates in order to price a bill of quantities.

This chapter considers the development of basic unit rates. Operational estimating, on the other hand, requires a deeper understanding of the relationship between estimating and project planning, and these issues are discussed in detail in Chapters 5 and 6.

4.2 NET OR GROSS PRICING

In simple terms, 'net' or 'gross' pricing refers to the individual firm's policy regarding the inclusion within the estimate, and perhaps within the priced bill of quantities, of allowances for overheads and profit. While the overall assessment of the overheads and profit element to be included in a tender forms part of management's adjudication function, firms differ in the way that these components are assessed and included in the estimate and/or priced bills of quantities.

In the case of *net* estimating, estimators make no allowance in their calculations for the overheads and profit elements. These items are then assessed during the adjudication stage, and are subsequently added to the estimator's total net cost for the whole project to give the final tender figure. The rates for measured work included in the priced bills of quantities may be left *net* (i.e. excluding any element of overheads and profit) and with the overheads and profit element included elsewhere (for example in the Preliminaries bill), or alternatively the total of the overheads and profit contribution in the project as a whole may be distributed over the rates in some way, for example as a percentage addition. In this latter case the bill is priced *gross* (i.e. the rates include some element for overheads and profit).

In the case of *gross* estimating, the prices calculated by the estimator include some predetermined standard percentage allowance for overheads and profit. The overall estimate, including allowances for overheads and profit, is then considered by management, and the adjudication stage consists of determining a lump sum to be added to, or subtracted from, the overall estimate to give the final tender figure, with the individual item rates being adjusted accordingly.

Both net and gross methods are in common use, and their use is generally a matter of preference for individual firms, although it is held by some that net pricing may give a slightly more accurate overall estimate due to the absence of rounding errors.

The factors to be considered in the adjudication process, and consideration of the distribution of the total tender sum across the various items in the bill of quantities are both considered in detail in Chapter 11.

4.3   RESOURCE COSTS

Excluding overheads and profit, the basic resources that the estimator needs to consider in pricing any construction work, irrespective of whether unit rate or operational techniques are used, are the quantities and costs of labour, plant and materials required to complete the work. The estimator therefore needs a clear understanding of these factors regardless of the specific type of work to be priced, and each of these factors is now considered in detail.

4.3.1   The Cost of Labour

Labour costs account for a major component of virtually all construction work. Fox and Gilleard (1992), for example, estimate labour costs as between 22% and 45% of overall project costs in Hong Kong. It is therefore obvious that a reasonably correct and accurate assessment of the cost of labour is fundamental to the accuracy of the estimate, but it is also generally accepted that the labour element is probably the most difficult component to estimate with any reasonable degree of accuracy.

Labour may either be directly employed by the contractor or, perhaps more commonly now, may be employed on a subcontract basis. In the case of subcontract labour, operatives will normally be self-employed and will normally give a lump sum price either for a complete parcel of work or for some pre-defined unit. A common example might be a bricklaying gang who might quote a rate per thousand bricks laid. In this case the estimator will simply include the appropriate labour price in the calculations. The advantages and disadvantages of using subcontract labour are considered in detail in Chapter 7.

In the case of directly employed labour, however, the situation is rather more complicated, in that the total labour cost for a given piece of work will consist of a combination of the 'all-in' hourly rate and the estimated production rate.

The 'all-in' hourly rate is defined as the total hourly cost of employing labour, and will therefore include any additional costs for which the employer is responsible in addition to the basic rate. These additional costs will vary from country to country, and in some instances from place to place, and may arise as a result of legislation (for example employers' National Insurance contributions), as a result of national or local wage settlement agreements reached between groups of employers and labour organisations, such as trade unions (for example payment of tool and clothing allowances), or as a result of the state of the local labour market (for example the need to pay an attraction bonus over and above the agreed minimum wage in order to attract workers to move from other employers).

In the UK, construction employers are bound not only by the relevant employment legislation, but also by the terms of the Working Rule Agreement entered into between the Union of Construction and Allied Trades and the Building Employers Confederation. Although this may appear to make life complicated for the estimator, in reality the British system is fairly straightforward. Some indication of how difficult things can become in other parts of the world is given by Barrie and Paulson (1992, p. 219):

> Estimating the money component of labor costs is more difficult in construction than in any other United States industry. Reasons for this situation include the scope and variety of the work involved, the craft nature of the labor unions, and the regional and local autonomy of labor and employer collective bargaining units. There are literally thousands of different wage rates, fringe benefits, insurance rates, and work rules, and there are exceptions to almost all of them. Superimposed upon this are federal, state, and local laws, taxes, and special programs such as wage and price control.

In the United Kingdom, the Working Rule Agreement is published annually by the National Joint Council for the Building Industry. Where this agreement

Table 4.1 Factors to be considered in the cost of labour

Overtime payments for time worked in excess of the agreed working hours
Public holidays
Guaranteed minimum weekly earnings
Bonus payments
Tool and clothing allowances
Annual holidays with pay scheme
Retirement and death benefit scheme
Travelling time, fares and lodging allowances
Injury and sickness benefit
National Insurance contributions
Construction Industry Training Board levy
Employer's liability insurance

applies, in addition to the basic labour rate, the all-in labour cost must take account of the items shown in Table 4.1.

Other factors, such as payments for continuous skill and responsibility or additional payments for work executed in difficult conditions will normally be added to the all-in hourly rate for the particular items to which they specifically apply.

CIOB (1983) includes a comprehensive example of an all-in hourly rate calculation. Others, for example McCaffer and Baldwin (1984), Mudd (1984), Bentley (1987), Cooke (1992), Brook (1993), Buchan *et al.* (1993) and Illingworth (1993), have all proposed minor variations on the same theme. Tables 4.2 and 4.3 show a typical example of the calculation of hours worked per year and the all-in hourly rate.

4.3.2   Estimating the Productivity of Labour

In addition to the 'all-in' hourly labour rate, the estimated costs for labour must also take into account the time which operatives will take to complete the various items of work, and it therefore also necessary to make some estimate of labour productivity.

General 'rules of thumb' for estimating labour productivity have long been used in the construction industry. Old sayings such as 'starting from scratch a joiner may make a four panel door in a day', or 'bricklayers lay a brick a minute' were once useful and well accepted estimating principles, and have now almost become part of the folklore of the industry. Perhaps it is as a consequence of this 'folklore' element that there is still a common belief that all estimators have an in-depth, encyclopaedic and accurate knowledge of production rates for all items of construction work. Ashworth and Skitmore,

Table 4.2 - Typical calculation of hours worked/paid per week

	Hours worked	Hours paid
Basic hours 39 h/wk × 48 wks/yr	1872	1872
Overtime (time and a half) say 2 h/day × 5 days/wk × 48 wks/yr	480	720
	2352	2592
Less		
Public holidays 8 days/yr × 10 h/day (overtime not paid)	80	24
Time lost for inclement weather say 2% of time worked	say 50	
Sick days say 5 days/yr × 10 h/day (including overtime allowance)	50	55
Total per year	2172	2513
Total hours/week	45.25	52.35

for example, refer to estimators' standard outputs being contained in their jealously guarded 'black book', and they further comment that such data are rarely if ever amended or revised. Those estimators who do not possess a personal 'black book' can gain some guidance on production rates for a huge variety of construction tasks from the many builders' price books published annually, such as those published by, among others, Spon, Wessex, Laxton and Griffiths.

While there is no doubt that 'standard' production information of this type is useful in providing a general idea of possible production rates, it is important to understand that the figures given are, at best, single-point averages of averages, and therefore represent only a guide to the average work rate which might be achieved under ideal conditions. There is no indication given of the possible spread that might occur on either side of the average. While there is little doubt that, in order to be effective, the estimator must have a good idea of the kind of average production rates that might be achieved, and the 'little black book' or the standard price book can perhaps give some guidance in this respect, it is also plainly nonsense to pretend that any forecasts based on such general information would prove to be acceptably accurate in any specific case. Adrian (1982, p. 154) makes the point that:

Table 4.3 - Calculation of 'all-in' hourly rate

	Skilled	Unskilled
Basic weekly wage	161.25	137.43
Tool and clothing allowance say	1.00	1.00
Gross wage	162.25	138.43
Bonus (say 25% of basic rate)	40.31	34.36
Sick pay say	1.30	1.30
National Insurance (9% of gross wages)	14.60	12.37
Holidays with pay scheme	19.20	19.20
Employer's liability insurance and redundancy fund (say 4% of gross wages)	6.49	5.53
	234.15	211.19
CITB levy (say 0.25% of payroll)	0.58	0.53
	234.73	211.72
All-in hourly rate = weekly cost/hours worked	£5.18	£4.68

While it is an important ingredient in an accurate estimate, past data alone will not ensure an accurate estimate. Each new project is affected by factors or parameters unique to an individual project.... A contractor should be aware of each of these factors or characteristics when determining the labor cost for each and every work item in his estimate.

It is therefore clearly apparent that the estimator must acquire sufficient knowledge of construction technology and construction techniques, and develop a sufficient degree of professional skill and judgement to assess the work rates that might be applicable to any particular situation.

The obvious way to assess labour productivity accurately might appear to be to collect data from completed work, and it is often said that the monitoring and coordination of such site feedback ought to be part of the estimator's role. Adrian (1982, p. 31 *et seq.*), for example, asserts that 'An important component of any estimating system is the collection of past project data and the structuring of the data for use in estimating future projects' and he goes on to construct an elaborate technique to model construction method productivity. Williams (1981) studied the relationship between estimating and work study in some depth, and concluded that it was essential to develop a good working relationship between estimators and work study officers in order that estimators could make maximum use of the data available. The estimator, however, faces a number of severe problems associated with the collection of site feedback of this kind:

1. In many, perhaps the majority of, companies the estimator's main interest and involvement with a project ends at the time the tender is submitted. Although, in the case of a successful project, the estimator may be involved in the preparation of the priced bills following acceptance of the tender, general commercial pressures will mean that by this stage the estimator will have moved on to price the next project. The estimator is not usually involved with the running of the project on site and must therefore rely on obtaining feedback from others in the construction team. Most contractors do not have the mechanisms in place to allow collection of the necessary data in a meaningful way, and the only feedback which tends to reach the estimator is negative, for example where the cost of the work on site exceeds the amount allowed in the estimate and someone is called to take the blame.

2. It is generally appreciated within the industry that productivity figures are very variable, and will be greatly affected by factors such as the degree of difficulty of the work, working conditions, learning curves, regional variations, the amount of disruption, the overall task duration and the gang composition. Some of these factors, for example optimum gang size, can be identified from work study exercises, and may be identified for new projects as part of the pre-tender planning process, but even then a substantial degree of uncertainty remains. As an example of the degree of variation that can occur, Fox and Gilleard (1992), commenting on a study by Horner (1990), report that:

> …the productivity of a single gang of bricklayers was found to vary by as much as 200% from one day to the next. In addition, compara-tive productivity rates between gangs was found during the study to vary by as much as 65% while carrying out similar activity under identical conditions.

3. Construction is generally a long-term process. The time taken from preparation of estimate until the time the work is carried out on site will generally be measured in months or even years. On the other hand, site feedback, if it is to be useful to the estimator for pricing future projects, must be provided as quickly as possible.

These factors have generally meant that, in the past, site feedback to the estimator has been both erratic and of doubtful accuracy, and it is no doubt for these reasons that estimators generally have tended not to place too much reliance on the information they do receive. Small wonder then that Ashworth and Skitmore report that:

> Investigation… has shown that if feedback ever does reach the estimator it is more often than not ignored. It is assumed that it relates to a one-off occurrence, and is, therefore, not relevant to the estimator's future work.

Despite the above comments there is no doubt that, in theory at least, accurate and timely site feedback would be of great benefit to the estimator, if not as a check on the detailed pricing of individual items then perhaps more importantly as a check on overall pricing levels.

Many different techniques for the measurement of labour productivity already exist, both in construction (for example Price and Harris (1985); Fox and Gilleard (1992)) and in other branches of engineering, but simple collection of the information is not enough. The information is of no value unless systems are in place for the data to be stored, analysed, correlated and interpreted. As Park (1979, p. 184) points out:

> Information is like garbage – it should not be collected until arrangements have been made for its disposition. Unless there is some place to put it after it has been collected, some way to find it when it is needed, and some useful purpose for it after it has been found information has little value for anyone.

Development of the necessary management information systems required involves a considerable investment in time and resources, an investment which, it would appear, many construction companies do not consider to be worthwhile at the present time. The situation may change with the development of more sophisticated computer based systems.

It will be apparent from the above that the estimation of labour costs can be subject to considerable uncertainty, and that this uncertainty will be increased on projects that are 'out of the ordinary'. In essence, the best that the estimator can do is to make an educated guess at probable labour productivity rates. The management of risk and uncertainty in the estimating and tendering processes is considered in Chapter 12.

Many of these problems can be overcome to some extent by the judicious use of labour-only subcontractors working for a fixed price, but this also carries with it some additional risks. The factors to be considered in the use of subcontractors are considered in more detail in Chapter 7.

4.3.3   The Cost of Materials

Costs for materials will almost always be derived from current quotations obtained specifically for a particular project. In most cases a number of suppliers will be invited to give a price, thus introducing, in theory at least, some element of competition. In some cases the estimator will be responsible for sending out the necessary enquiries, but many larger companies will employ a specialist buyer.

There are a number of important factors to be considered when estimating costs for materials.

1. *The units in which materials are bought and the units in which measured items are measured are sometimes not the same*

Because items measured in bills of quantities generally represent the finished work fixed in place, it is often the case that the units of measure do not correspond with the units in which the materials are bought. Examples might be brickwork, measured in m^2 whereas bricks are bought by the thousand, or hardcore measured in m^2 or m^3 but bought by the tonne. The estimator must therefore convert the measured quantity into a suitable form to invite quotations.

2. *Work is usually measured net*

Under most Standard Methods of Measurement construction work is measured net fixed in place. The consequence of this is that no allowance is made in the measured quantities for waste, for laps on sheet materials or, on bulk materials such as concrete, for consolidation and shrinkage. Where laps are required the necessary information will usually be given either in the description or in the specification. The quantities given in the bills will therefore often be considerably less than the contractor needs to buy to complete the work and the cost of the extra materials required to cover these items must be allowed for in the rates. This is conventionally done by a percentage addition to net material cost, and in the case of laps is usually relatively easy to assess.

The addition for waste is rather more problematic. Material waste takes a number of forms, some of which are to do with the project and can therefore be relatively easily quantified. Examples would be *cutting waste* arising from the need to cut sheet materials to size and shape, or *residual waste*, where, for example, materials bought in sealed containers or required minimum quantities are not fully used in the work. Other types of waste, however, arise from the way materials are stored and handled on site, and are therefore greatly affected by the efficiency and organisation of the site management. Examples might be *stockpile waste* on bricks, where the bottom layers of material are damaged due to incorrect stacking, or *application waste*, where wet trade materials are lost through spillage or over-mixing. It is very difficult for estimators to make accurate allowances for these items since they will generally have no control over the site production process.

As with labour outputs, the theorists claim that factors such as waste allowances should ideally be assessed on the basis of site feedback, but it has already been shown that such feedback is rarely available. Estimators will therefore tend to rely on their own experience and some kind of 'standard' allowances, which are often insufficient.

3. *Delivery and handling*

Prices are often quoted by suppliers as 'ex-works'. This means that haulage from the supplier's depot to the site is excluded and must be allowed for separately. These costs can be considerable where heavy or bulky materials are concerned. In addition, even where prices include delivery to site, it is likely that for bulk materials quoted prices will exclude off-loading and handling, and the estimator must again allow for these factors separately. Some delivery vehicles, for example brick lorries, will usually be equipped with mechanical handling equipment, for which an additional charge is usually made, but it may also be necessary in some cases to allow for off-loading using labourers, or a fork lift stacker truck.

4. *Discounts*

A complex system of trade discounts exists within the materials supply industry, and the 'list price' of materials will usually be considerably higher than the 'net' price the contractor will have to pay. Discounts available may vary greatly depending upon the quantity ordered, the reputation of the contractor and current supply and demand conditions within the materials supply industry. The discounts available are very sensitive to changes in market conditions, and it is therefore important to obtain fresh quotations for each new project. The position should also be reviewed when the materials are actually ordered. Higher discounts are also often obtainable on materials that can be ordered in full loads directly from the manufacturers rather than through builders' merchants.

4.3.4   The Cost of Plant

It is less common nowadays for general contractors in construction to own substantial items of plant. Large items of plant represent a substantial investment, and most contractors will not have a sufficiently smooth flow of work to keep the plant working at peak efficiency. It is therefore more common for contractors to hire plant as and when required from a specialist plant hire company. Even in those cases where contractors do own their own plant it is now common for that part of the business to operate as a separate plant hire subsidiary, hiring plant to particular projects as and when required at some predetermined rate. The main exception might be where a contractor has a large civil engineering scheme, in which case it might be more economical to purchase new plant specifically for the project, write off the cost over the period of the project and then sell it off again at the end.

In the case of plant hired in from an outside firm, the estimator will need to decide what additional costs need to be added to the basic hire rates to make up the 'all-in' cost, for example the cost of the operator, fuel and transport for the plant to and from the site.

Where a piece of plant is used for a number of specific items of work, for example a site-based concrete mixing plant, the costs may be apportioned among the various bill items involved and included in the unit rates. In other cases, for example a tower crane, a breakdown of the cost between specific items of work may be impractical, and the cost may then be included elsewhere, perhaps in the Preliminaries section of the bill.

4.4   SYNTHESIS OF UNIT RATES

Accepting the problems outlined above, in principle the synthesis of unit rates simply requires that the estimator add together the costs of all of the labour, plant and materials required to complete a given item of work. This apparently simple process of course implies that the estimator has the necessary skills and detailed knowledge to identify all of the various items to be included in any particular unit rate. Many authors (see for example Mudd (1984), Bentley (1987) and Buchan et al. (1993) among others) have already published estimating textbooks giving detailed unit rate calculations for many different building trades, while McCaffer and Baldwin (1984) provide a similar text for civil engineering. It is not the intention here to duplicate their work by presenting either a comprehensive account of the specific problems that confront the estimator in pricing each and every different trade, or to give detailed unit rate calculations for numerous different construction activities. What is considered important, however, is that the underlying principles should be clearly understood, and for that reason a condensed overview of the basic techniques is given here with the aid of a few typical examples. An example of a simple unit rate calculation is are shown in Table 4.4.

In some cases elements of the calculation may be common in the calculation of rates for several items. Table 4.5 for example shows part of a bill of quantities for brickwork, from which it is evident that a number of items all use the same mix of mortar.

In this case it therefore makes sense to calculate the m^3 cost of mixed mortar first as a pre-analysis rate (see Table 4.6) and then to use this in the

Table 4.4 Simple concrete work unit rate calculation

Bill description			
Concrete grade 25/20 in foundations in trenches (m³)			
Method			
Use ready-mixed concrete discharged directly into trench			
Material			£
Ready mix discharged into trench	1 m³	£35.00	35.00
Waste	5%		1.75
			36.75
Labour			
Concretor placing concrete	1.25 h/m³	£6.00	7.50
Plant – Nil			
	Unit Rate/m³		£44.25

detailed calculation of rates for each of the brickwork items. Although the example shown in Table 4.6 is simple to show the technique, pre-analysis rates can become very complex. The pre-analysis to calculate the ex-mixer costs of a number of different concrete mixes to be supplied by a site batching plant, for example, might include the cost of erecting the plant, operation for a period of time assessed from the concrete placement programme and subsequent final dismantling and removal.

Some typical examples of unit rate calculations for brickwork are shown in Table 4.7.

In some cases the units of measure used in the bills of quantities are not compatible with the units of work output which the estimator might want to use, and in addition some aspects of the work might be left to the contractor's discretion. As an example, consider the item for drain trench excavation shown in Table 4.8.

In this case the trench is measured in the bill of quantities in metres, with the width of the trench left to the contractor's discretion. Assuming that the work will be carried out by machine, the estimator must first make some assumptions about the method of working. Drain trenches are commonly excavated with a back-actor, and in this case the estimator will also need to make some assumptions about the width of bucket to be used. In this case the assumption is made that this item is one of a number of items of different depths included in the bill, and that the machine will be able to excavate them

Table 4.5 Typical brickwork entries in bill of quantities

	F: Masonry	
	F10: Brick and block walling	
	Common brickwork, BS 3921 in gauged mortar 1:2:9	
	Walls	
a	half brick thick	95 m^2
b	one brick thick	40 m^2
	Composite work; English bond; common brickwork, BS3921; facing bricks, Classbrick Smooth Red Pressed; in gauged mortar 1:2:9	
	Walls	
c	one and a half brick thick; facings one side; common brickwork finished fair one side	65 m^2
	Facing brickwork; Classbrick Smooth Red Pressed; in gauged mortar 1:2:9	
	Walls	
d	half brick thick; facework one side	74 m^2
e	one brick thick; facework both sides	57 m^2

all to the same width. In addition, although the trench is measured in metres, is more convenient for the estimator to work mainly in cubic metres.

The calculation of the unit rates themselves is clearly seen to be largely an arithmetical process, and many estimators now use computer-based spreadsheet programs as a matter of course. In practice, however, in order to make the assumptions necessary to support the calculations, the estimator will require considerable knowledge of construction technology and working methods, and it is perhaps for this reason that it is sometimes said that the best qualification for an estimator is experience of the industry. The estimator will also require a good working knowledge of the appropriate Standard Methods of Measurement, particularly regarding items which, although not specifically mentioned in the bills of quantities are nevertheless deemed to be included in the unit rates. The various Standard Methods of Measurement frequently have differing provisions; the General Rules section of the *Standard Method of Measurement for Building Works*: Seventh edition (RICS, 1988, p. 12 clause 4.6) for example is quite precise:

Table 4.6 Example of pre-analysis rate

Pre-analysis rates – Gauged mortar mix 1:2:9			
Basis of analysis 1m^3 of wet mortar			
Materials			£
Cement delivered and unloaded	0.19 tns	£66.60	12.65
Sand	1.81 tns	£9.00	16.29
Lime delivered and unloaded	0.18 tns	£83.60	15.04
			43.98
Plant			
Included in Preliminaries			–
Labour			
Mixer operated by bricklayers' labourer – cost included in gang rate			–
Cost/m^3 of mixed mortar			43.98

Unless otherwise specifically stated in a bill of quantities or herein, the following shall be deemed to be included with all items:

(a) Labour and all costs in connection therewith.

(b) Materials, goods and all costs in connection therewith.

(c) Assembling, fitting and fixing materials and goods in position.

(d) Plant and all costs in connection therewith.

(e) Waste of materials.

(f) Square cutting

(g) Establishment charges, overhead charges and profit.

The *Principles of Measurement (International) for Works of Construction* (RICS, 1979, p. 1 clause GP4.1), however, is much less precise:

Unless otherwise stated, *all items shall be fully inclusive of all that is necessary to fulfil the liabilities and obligations arising out of the contract* [author's italics] and shall include:

1. Labour and all associated costs

2. Materials, goods and all associated costs

Table 4.7 Example of brickwork unit rate analysis

<u>Brickwork unit rate analysis</u>
<u>Method statement</u>

Use 2 and 1 gang – all-in cost per trowel £9.30

<u>Item a – half brick thick wall in common bricks</u>

Basis of analysis 1 m^2

		£
Materials		
Common bricks (delivered and unloaded)	60 nr × £131.37/1000	7.88
Waste on bricks say	7.5%	0.59
Mortar (assume no frogs)	0.017 m^3 × £43.98	0.75
Waste on mortar say	10%	0.08
Total materials		9.30

Labour		
Assume 45 bricks/h per trowel	1.33 h × £9.30	12.37
Rate/m^2		21.67

<u>Item c – one and a half brick thick composite wall faced one side, fair faced one side</u>

Basis of analysis 1 m^2

<u>Materials</u>

Common bricks (delivered and unloaded)	180 nr × £131.37/1000	23.65
Facing bricks (delivered and unloaded)		
Facings	£356.37/1000	
Commons	£131.37/1000	
Extra over cost	£225.00/1000	
	90 nr × £225.00/1000	20.03
Waste on bricks say	7.5% on £43.68	3.28
Mortar (assume no frogs)	0.072 m^3 × £43.98	3.17
Waste on mortar say	10%	0.32
Total materials		50.45

Labour		
Assume 55 bricks/h for basic wall	3.27 h	
Extra for facings and pointing	0.20 h	
Extra for fair face on commons	0.10 h	
	3.57 h × £9.30	33.20
Rate/m^2		83.65

Table 4.8 Example of unit rate calculation for drainage trench

Excavate trench; drain pipe not exceeding 200 mm nominal diameter; average depth 750 mm

Method statement

Inspection of the tender information shows that the ground is firm clay and therefore no earthwork support is required. Excavation will be 450 mm wide using a back-actor, disposal of surplus material by spreading on site adjacent to the trench, backfill first 300 mm by hand, remainder by machine compacted in 150 mm layers.

Basis of analysis 10 m. Bulking factor for excavated material 30%, compaction factor 20%.

Pre-analysis

Volume of trench excavation per 10 m run $10 \times 0.45 \times 0.75 = \underline{3.375\ m^3}$
Volume of hand backfill (less pipe)
$\qquad (10 \times 0.45 \times 0.3) - (10 \times 0.10 \times 0.10 \times \pi) = 1.036\ m^3$
$\qquad 1.036 + 20\% = \underline{1.24\ m^3}$
Volume of machine backfill $10 \times 0.45 \times 0.45 = 2.025 + 20\% = \underline{2.43\ m^3}$
Area for compaction of filling (in 150 mm layers $10 \times 0.45 \times 4 = \underline{18\ m^2}$

Unit rate analysis

Plant (including fuel and driver)			£
Excavator (assume 6 m³/h)	3.375 m³ × 6	0.56 h	
Backfill (assume 8 m³/h)	2.43 m³ × 8	0.30 h	
		0.86 h × £12.50	10.75
Vibro-roller (assume 10 m²/h)		18 m² × £4.50	8.10
Labour			
Banksman attendance on excavator		0.86 h	
Trim trench bottom	4.50 m² × 0.22 h/m²	0.99 h	
Hand backfill	1.24 m³ × 1 h/m³	1.24 h	
Compact backfill with roller		1.80 h	
		4.89 h × £4.95	24.21
	Rate for 10 m =		43.06
	Rate/m = £4.31		

3. Provision of plant

4. Temporary works

5. Establishment charges, overheads and profit

In addition to these general clauses there may be other requirements either included in the Rules for Measurement or written into the preambles section of the bills of quantities. In SMM7 these requirements are included in the coverage rules for each work section, and may in some cases be extensive. SMM7 Section F, Masonry coverage rule C1 for example states that rates for brickwork and blockwork are deemed to include:

(a) extra materials for curved work

(b) all rough and fair cutting

(c) forming rough and fair grooves, throats, mortices, chases, rebates and holes, stops and mitres

(d) raking out joints to form a key

(e) labours in eaves filling

(f) labours in returns, ends and angles

(g) centring

Familiarity with whatever Method of Measurement has been used to prepare the tender document is obviously essential.

4.5   ACCURACY OF UNIT RATES

A UK study of 40 building contracts by the Property Services Agency in the course of development of their significant items estimating technique (PSA, 1987) showed that 20% of the most cost-significant items in a typical bill of quantities amounted to between 69% (plumbing and glazing) and 87% (brickwork) of the total value of the relevant measured works section. In terms of the bill as a whole, 78% of the total value of measured work was accounted for by the top 20% of items, thus confirming the historically generally accepted view that the Pareto principle (Haney, 1970, pp. 837–9, Dell'Isola, 1982, p. 68) generally applies to the distribution of costs in a typical bill of quantities for building works, although this is almost certainly not the case in civil engineering.

While the 80:20 relationship may not be absolutely accurate, and may in any case have changed with the introduction of SMM7, which eliminated the separate measurement of large numbers of work items of low value, it is nonetheless true that the majority of the tender cost in most bills will be accounted for by a relatively small proportion of high value items. This is apparently well recognised and reflected in current estimating practice; Skitmore and Wilcox (1994) for example report that their study of the estimating practices of smaller builders, although based on a very small sample, suggested that estimators apply non-detailed methods for up to 50% of bill items; in other words, they only calculate unit rates for something like half of the items in a typical measured bill. Skitmore and Wilcox survey also suggests that the main criterion in deciding whether or not a detailed unit rate should be calculated is the total value of the particular item in cash terms (i.e. the item rate multiplied by the item quantity). This judgement appears to be highly subjective and to be made with no objective consideration of the cost relationship between the item value, the section value and/or the total project value.

Nonetheless, it is clearly these high-value items to which the estimator must obviously address the most attention. In general the estimator's rates for these items should be as accurate as they can be, bearing in mind the problems outlined earlier, and should therefore be the subject of a full unit rate analysis such as those shown earlier. Items of lesser value, however, may not justify the full treatment and can often be priced with much less effort either by experience or by the addition of a percentage of the major item cost.

4.6   REFERENCES

Ashworth A. and Skitmore R.M. *Accuracy in Estimating*, Occasional Paper No. 27, The Chartered Institute of Building, London.

Barrie D.S. and Paulson B.C. (1992) *Professional Construction Management*, McGraw-Hill, New York.

Bentley J.I.W. (1987) *Construction Tendering and Estimating*, E. & F.N. Spon, London.

Brook M. (1993) *Estimating and tendering for Construction Work*, Butterworth-Heinemann, Oxford.

Buchan R.D., Fleming F.W. and Kelly J.R. (1993) *Estimating for Builders and Quantity Surveyors*, Newnes, London.

CIOB (1983) *Code of Estimating Practice*, The Chartered Institute of Building, London.

Cooke B. (1992) *Contract Planning and Contractual Procedures*, 3rd edn, Macmillan, London.

Dell'Isola A.J. (1982) *Value Engineering in the Construction Industry*, Van Nostrand Reinhold, New York.

Fox P.W. and Gilleard J.D. (1992) 'Measuring labour productivity in construction firms', *Hong Kong Engineer*, February 1992.

Haney L.H. (1970) *History of Economic Thought – a Critical Account of the Origin and Development of the Economic Theories of the Leading Thinkers in the Leading Nations*, Macmillan, New York.

Horner R.M.W. (1990) 'Causes of variability in bricklayer's productivity, *Building Economics and Construction Management*, Proc. CIB '90 symposium, Sydney, Australia, pp. 238–50.

Illingworth J.R. (1993) *Construction Methods and Planning*, E & F.N. Spon, London.

McCaffer R. and Baldwin A. (1984) *Estimating and Tendering for Civil Engineering Works*, Granada Technical Books, London.

Mudd D.R. (1984) *Estimating and Tendering for Construction Work*, Butterworth, London.

Park W.R. (1979) *Construction Bidding for Profit*, John Wiley, New York.

Price A.D. and Harris F.C. (1985) *Methods of Measuring Production Times for Construction Work*, Technical Information Service No. 49, Chartered Institute of Building, London.

PSA (1987) *Significant Items Estimating*, Department of the Environment Property Services Agency, London.

RICS (1979) *Principles of Measurement (International) for Works of Construction,* The Royal Institution of Chartered Surveyors, London.

RICS (1988) *Standard Method of Measurement of Building Works*, 7th edn, The Royal Institution of Chartered Surveyors, London.

Skitmore M. and Wilcox J. (1994) 'Estimating processes of smaller builders', *Construction Management and Economics*, Vol. 12, pp. 139–54.

5   Estimating and Planning

5.1   INTRODUCTION

This chapter considers the relationship between the estimating and planning functions within a contractor's organisation during the estimating and tendering stages of a project. It does not attempt to provide detailed descriptions of the operation and use of alternative planning techniques, merely to explore the relationship between overall project time, cost and tender price from the estimator's point of view, and to highlight some of the more important project planning issues which need to be considered in the preparation of a tender bid.

5.2   THE RELATIONSHIP BETWEEN TIME AND COST

The previous chapter considered the build-up of basic rates largely in isolation, the only mention of time being in connection with the assessment of likely labour productivity. In practice this is, of course, totally unrealistic; the existence of a relationship between time and cost is well known. There will, for both parties to the contract, always be an optimum time for completion of a project at lowest cost, but the problem is that the client's optimum time might not be the same as the contractor's. In a competitive tendering situation therefore, particularly where lowest price is likely to be the most significant criterion, sensible contractors aiming to submit competitive prices ought at least to know what their optimum time for lowest cost will be. It is also in the client's interest in assessing tenders to be as sure as possible that the contractor can complete the work within the proposed time-scale, and some clients may therefore ask for an outline project programme to be provided as part of the tender submission.

In many projects time will be prescribed by the client in the tender documents, and this will inevitably have an effect on cost. As an example, consider a contract to construct new mass reinforced concrete machine bases in an existing factory. In the absence of any time constraints the price can be calculated easily enough using unit rates built up from 'standard' production rates, but consider the position if the client needs the whole of the work to be completed during the annual two-week holiday shutdown period. Such a requirement may well mean a 'crash' programme involving 24 hour-a-day shift working, consequent payments for overtime, increased labour gang strengths resulting in lower productivity per man, out of sequence working etc., all of which will inevitably increase the cost.

At the other end of the scale, consider a contract for the construction of a new school. In this case the client may not want to take possession of the building until just before the start of the new school year; a new building half-way through the year may be of no use. This information is again likely to be reflected in the contract period stated in the tender documentation. It is accepted here that the Standard Forms of Building Contract require the client to take possession of the building upon certification of practical completion, and that the date for completion stated in the contract documents is usually the last date by which the project must be completed. If the contractor finishes early the client could be placed in the position of having to take possession of the school even though there is no immediate need for it, but it is worth remembering that it is the architect's responsibility to certify practical completion, and that there will almost always be some item of work which is either incomplete or unsatisfactory which can be used as a reason for non-certification. This may in turn mean that the contractor will be required to maintain the site organisation for longer than the optimum time, thus again giving rise to increased costs.

It is therefore evident that costs will rise if the work has to be completed before or after the contractor's optimum completion time. The relationship is discussed at length by Hillebrandt (1974), and is shown in outline in Figure 5.1 (adapted from Hillebrandt), where line A–B shows the contractor's time/cost curve, with optimum completion at point P1. Line E–F shows the client's time/cost curve for a project required on a specific date (P2), for example the school mentioned above, and line C–D shows the time/cost relationship for a client requiring completion as early as possible. A number of writers (for example Rosenblatt and Roll (1985); Sule and Chow (1992)) have proposed mathematical models for determining optimum project duration taking into account the likely costs of acceleration and delay, but there is little evidence of the active application of such techniques on a regular basis in construction.

Any estimate of price for construction work must therefore pay due attention to the time requirements and proposed construction methods, and estimating must therefore be carried out hand in hand with project planning. Baxendale (1991) contends that cost information cannot be meaningful unless it is related to a time frame, while Schuette and Liska (1994, p. 59), although writing for an American audience, still put the point exceptionally well:

> The estimate should reflect the method of construction. Different construction methods dictate unique productivity rates and equipment

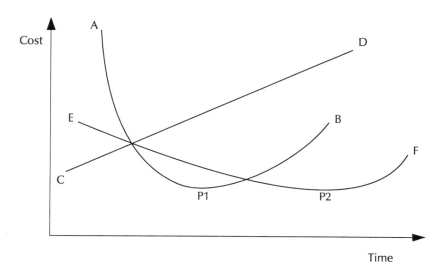

Figure 5.1   Optimum project completion times (after Hillebrandt (1974)

requirements. In addition, the construction schedule indicates the duration of the project. This is useful to the estimator when calculating the cost of overhead items such as the project superintendent, job site office, and temporary utilities. A plan of construction activities should be developed during the estimating process.

Spon (1994, p. 3), in the context of civil engineering work, goes even further and sees the preparation of the plan as a necessary prerequisite to the estimate:

To prepare a price for a civil engineering project, then it is necessary to have regard to the method to be adopted in executing the work, draw up a detailed programme and then cost out the resources necessary to prosecute the chosen method.

This chapter therefore considers the following issues in respect of the pre-tender planning stage:

1. The purpose(s) of the pre-tender plan

2. The degree of detail required

3. Appropriate techniques

4. Who produces the plan?

5. Method statements

5.3   THE PURPOSE OF THE PRE-TENDER PLAN

The basic purposes of the pre-tender plan are to identify:

1. A realistic project time frame

2. The methods to be used in carrying out the work

3. The resources necessary in order to complete the work within the required time frame

As far as the project time-scale is concerned, the programme must identify the optimum time frame for lowest cost (i.e. assuming the most economical use of resources), and this will then allow the estimator to judge whether or not any time frame quoted in the tender documentation is reasonably achievable. The project time-scale will also indicate the length of time 'preliminaries' (items such as site offices and site foremen) will be required to be maintained on site and, in conjunction with the associated resource data, will allow the estimator to develop a provisional cash flow forecast. This information can then be used to forecast the financing requirements of the project and any consequent costs.

If the time frame quoted in the tender documentation differs greatly from the optimum shown by the proposed construction programme and resource analysis, the estimator must decide how the additional costs are to be incorporated into the tender bid. A number of strategies are possible. If, for example, the project is required to be completed in a much shorter time than the optimum shown by the programme, then the obvious solution is, wherever possible, to adjust the resource data used to compute the unit rates to reflect the shorter programme, for example by including overtime payments etc., but there may be other considerations.

It is possible, for example, in a competitive climate, that the estimator may be required to provide a comparative assessment of the additional costs involved in meeting the client's required completion date (shift working, overtime etc.) with the costs which the contractor would be likely to incur in payment for liquidated damages if the work were to be completed late. This calculation, or perhaps commercial judgement would be a better term, can incorporate many subjective factors. On the one hand the contractor will need to consider the 'worth' of completing the project on time in terms of enhanced reputation with the client, likelihood of repeat orders etc. On the other hand, however, contractors know that the liquidated damages provisions included in the Standard Forms of Building Contract are not mandatory, and they will therefore make an assessment of the likelihood that the employer will actually invoke the contractual provisions. Also to be considered will be the state of the tender documentation and the likelihood of being able to claim extensions of time during the course of the work. A very significant factor in the adjudication stage may be the thought that including the true costs of completing the work on time may render the contractor's bid uncompetitive in comparison with competitors taking a more 'commercial' view of the above issues.

In the case of projects where the client's time frame exceeds the programmed optimum, most contractors will tend to quote a price based on the optimum period. There may be some justification for this view, since some commonly used forms of contract (e.g. JCT80) require the architect to issue a practical completion certificate as soon as the building is 'practically complete'. Practical completion is usually taken to mean that the building is sufficiently complete for the client to take possession and use the building as was originally intended in the contract. The only risks in this case from the contractor's point of view are that:

1. The architect will be able to provide all of the necessary information at the time required to meet the contractor's programme.

2. The architect will not be especially awkward about judging whether or not the works have, in the architect's opinion, reached practical completion.

Some contractors will attempt to formalise the position by attempting to persuade the client (or perhaps more likely the architect) to agree to an amended completion date before the contract is signed, but as pointed out earlier this may not always be in the client's interest. A full consideration of this issue from the client's point of view is not appropriate here, but Mendelsohn (1994) deals with the issue in some detail.

5.4   DEGREE OF DETAIL REQUIRED IN THE PRE-TENDER PLAN

It is generally considered that a contractor will place differing degrees of utility on the tenders submitted depending upon an assessment of the desirability of a particular project to the company and the chances of getting the job, and that this assessment of project utility is likely to affect the amount of resources that the contractor is prepared to invest in order to prepare a bid.

Cooke (1992, p. 11) sets out a typical strategy when he suggests that companies might 'grade' projects as follows:

Category A: Full treatment Anxious to obtain the work. Will submit a competitive bid. Likely to be adjudicated keenly.

Category B: Detailed estimate Prepared to invest reasonable effort to secure the work. Likely to be prepared to take the project on modest risk terms.

Category C: Routine estimate Adjudication likely to be such that the contract will only be taken at a good margin.

Category D: Minimal treatment Policy submission only with no real likelihood of getting the job.

Cooke goes on to suggest that only for projects in categories A and B will a significant planning effort be required, with only minimal attention being given to other projects, but this may be too simplistic an analysis. Contractors' decisions about the resources they need to commit may also be affected by factors such as the type and size of the project and their own familiarity with that particular type of work. There may be little need for detailed planning for a project where the work is very straightforward and is in an area where the contractor has extensive experience even if the contract is of relatively high value and is allocated a high degree of utility by the contractor. On the other hand, the preparation of a 'routine' estimate for a project of lower utility, but where the contractor has less experience, may require more detailed consideration. After all, as Mudd (1984, p. 25) points out:

> The efforts of construction management should be aimed not so much at establishing or confirming normal accepted practice but rather at highlighting critical factors and abnormal or unusual situations and providing solutions to overcome them.

Although Mueller (1986) argues that the only way to produce a meaningful estimate is by considering each and every separate activity required to complete the project, it is generally accepted that the degree of detail required in the pre-tender plan is rather less than that which will be required later in the post contract stage if the bid is successful. Brockfield (1981), however, considers that even the simplest pre-tender programme must, as an absolute minimum, consider the following factors:

1. The client's completion requirements together with any allowances for phasing and fitting out

2. Topography of the site, access, enabling works etc.

3. The form of construction (i.e. is it possible on a framed scheme to get the roof watertight before construction of the external walls?)

4. Continuity of work: is the work essentially cyclical (e.g. a multi-storey building with repetition on each floor) or linear?

5. The time of year: productivity may fall dramatically in the winter months unless the building can be made weathertight before the winter period.

In addition to a basic programme, resource analyses and method statements for the major items of work will be required. The pricing of the Preliminaries section (see Chapter 8) may also require the preparation of a site layout drawing showing the organisation and disposition of the contractor's temporary facilities, spoil heaps, access and haul roads etc.

In essence, at tender stage, the estimator is concerned with the big cost-significant items, overall time-scales and high-level strategic method statements, whereas the construction stage programme will be concerned with a much more detailed assessment of site coordination and control. It is also important to remember that time for compiling the estimate is almost always tight, and that management must be able to grasp the relevant issues quickly and accurately during the adjudication stage. There is therefore a strong need for pre-tender programme information to be presented in a simple, clear and concise summary form.

5.5 PLANNING TECHNIQUES

A basic knowledge of planning techniques is assumed, and a full consideration of the use and application of different planning techniques is therefore not appropriate here, but it is considered important to summarise some of the more significant issues arising from the use of common programming methods as they relate to estimating and tendering.

5.5.1 Bar or Gantt Charts

These have the advantage of simplicity. They are quick to prepare and in many cases enable the whole picture to be quickly appreciated by those without a detailed knowledge of planning techniques. It is, however, sometimes difficult to see the precise relationship between different activities, although this can to some extent be overcome by the use of linked charts. Large projects with a high degree of repetition, however, might be exceptionally difficult to model effectively in this way.

Bar charts are probably the most widely used form of programme at the pre-tender stage because of their comparative simplicity.

5.5.2 Network Analysis

Network analyses tend to be more complex and time-consuming to prepare in the first instance, but it is subsequently much easier to identify the critical activities and to find the critical path. Computer-based CPM or PERT type programmes which allow multiple durations (optimistic, pessimistic and most likely) to be entered for each activity can be useful in that they facilitate 'What if?' simulations of different strategies, and this can be useful in finding the optimum time period for minimum cost.

One problem with these techniques in the past has been the difficulty of assigning accurate durations to each activity. Overly optimistic durations can result in the project not being completed on time, whereas pessimistic durations can result in under-usage of resources. It is possible that contemporary research into computer-based planning methods will ease these problems. Wu and Hadipriono (1994) for example report the development of a computer-based decision support system for estimating activity durations using a 'fuzzy logic' approach. It is also known that at least one large CAD system developer is working on linking its CAD system to project planning and cost estimation software. Morad and Beliveau (1991) discuss, in some depth, the issue of current research regarding the integration of CAD with artificial intelligence to generate construction plans.

5.5.3   Line of Balance

The line of balance technique originated in manufacturing engineering, and while perhaps not as widely used in construction as bar charts and network analysis, is most useful for projects with a high degree of repetition, where bar charts or network analyses become overly complex and cumbersome to use.

5.6   WHO PREPARES THE PROGRAMME?

For large schemes it is usual for the programme to be prepared by a team of people headed by a specialist planning engineer with assistance from the estimator, plant manager, contracts manager etc. McCaffer and Baldwin (1984), reporting on a earlier study (Baldwin, 1982), write that a survey of 12 major civil engineering companies revealed that the most common approach was to have a planner and an estimator working in close liaison. However, while this might be the norm for large projects, it is likely that at the smaller end of the scale estimators may well be forced to rely on their own judgement and planning skills.

As an example, one project where the estimator was faced with preparing his own pre-tender programme concerned a contract for internal alterations to a branch of a major UK high street bank. The project entailed work throughout all three floors of the existing 100-year-old town centre building, which had to be completed while the bank remained in full operation. In order to achieve this the project was divided into six phases, each of which had to be completed and handed over before the next could begin. The contract was won by a medium-sized provincial contractor with a contract value, adjusted to 1994 prices, of approximately £0.6 m and a contract period of 12 months. The programming problems inherent in projects of this type are substantial, and tendering contractors must balance the risk of leaving the programming to the estimator against the cost of committing a planning engineer to assist.

5.7 METHOD STATEMENTS

Method statements form an essential part of the planning process and are complementary to the programme. While the detailed preparation of method statements is usually considered to be a matter for the planning engineer, it is important for the estimator to know what information the method statement can be expected to provide. Good examples of method statements may be found in, for example, Illingworth (1993) and Cooke (1992).

The purpose of the method statement at pre-tender stage from the estimator's point of view is to provide as detailed a statement as is possible of how the work will be carried out and the resources which will be required to achieve the end result. Method statements may be very simple or extremely complex, depending upon the work required, and are usually related to one or more site operations. It may therefore be extremely difficult to relate them directly to measured items in a bill of quantities.

Since the purpose of the method statement from the estimator's point of view is to provide details of the resources required from which the likely cost of the work can be estimated, it must, as a minimum, include:

1. A clear and concise description of the operation(s) and quantities of work included in order that the estimator can relate the work described as closely as possible to measured bill items.

2. A statement of the overall time allowance for the work.

3. A clear and concise description of the proposed method of construction, together with any alternative methods which the estimator may wish to consider.

4. An analysis of the plant required including the time each item is required on site.

5. A description of any temporary works required, including safety items; scaffolding is an obvious example.

6. An analysis of labour requirements, including number of gangs, gang strengths, anticipated work rates and the time each gang is required on site.

The worth to the estimator of accurate and well thought out method statements cannot be over-emphasised. Note also that method statements are not only required for large schemes; they may be equally important on smaller schemes, particularly those which pose unusual problems of time-scale or complexity. The method statement, together with the project programme, provides the basic framework from which the estimator can estimate the likely cost with the maximum degree of accuracy.

The logical method of estimating in conjunction with an operationally based programme is to price each operation as a separate item. This technique, called operational estimating, is considered in detail in Chapter 6.

5.8 REFERENCES

Baldwin A.N. (1982) Computer aided estimation for civil engineering contractors, *PhD Thesis*, Loughborough University of Technology, UK.

Baxendale A.T. (1991) 'Management information systems: the use of work breakdown structure in the integration of time and cost', in *Management, Quality and Economics in Building* (Bezalga A. and Brandon P. eds.), E. & F.N. Spon, London.

Brockfield W.F. (1981) 'Planning in relation to estimating', in *The Practice of Estimating*, Chartered Institute of Building, London.

Cooke B. (1992) *Contract Planning and Contractual Procedures*, 3rd edn, Macmillan, London.

Hillebrandt P.M. (1974) *Economic Theory and the Construction Industry*, Macmillan, London.

Illingworth J.R. (1993) *Construction Methods and Planning*, E. & F.N. Spon, London.

McCaffer R. and Baldwin A. (1984) *Estimating and Tendering for Civil Engineering Works*, Granada Technical Books, London.

Mendelsohn R. (1994) 'Early completion schedules: the promise and the pitfalls', *Journal of Management in Engineering*, February 1994, pp. 28–30 (American Society of Civil Engineers).

Morad A.A. and Beliveau Y.J. (1991) 'Knowledge based planning systems', *Journal of Construction Engineering and Management*, Vol. 117, No. 1, March 1991 (American Society of Civil Engineers).

Mudd D.R. (1984) *Estimating and Tendering for Construction Works*, Butterworth, London.

Mueller F.W. (1986) *Integrated Cost and Schedule Control for Construction Projects*, Van Nostrand Reinhold, New York.

Rosenblatt M.J. and Roll Y. (1985) 'A future value approach to determining project duration', *The Engineering Economist*, Vol. 17, No. 2, pp. 164–7.

Schuette S.D. and Liska R.W. (1994) *Building Construction Estimating*, McGraw Hill, New York.

Spon (1994) *Spon's Civil Engineering and Highway Works Price Book*, 8th edn, E. & F.N. Spon, London.

Sule D.R. and Chow B.H.B (1992) 'A present value approach to determine optimum project duration', *The Engineering Economist*, Vol. 37, No. 2, pp. 166–71.

Wu W.K.R. and Hadipriono F.C. (1994) 'Fuzzy modus ponens deduction technique for construction scheduling', *Journal of Construction Engineering and Management*, Vol. 120, No. 1, March 1994 (American Society of Civil Engineers).

6　Operational Estimating

6.1　INTRODUCTION

It has already been shown that the traditional 'unit rate' method of estimating is not particularly compatible with much of the resource-based information generated by the pre-contract planning process, and that, in the interests of accurate estimating, estimators may wish to price some parcels of work as a whole package rather than as a series of separate items. This method is termed operational estimating. One common example might be earthworks using heavy plant. In this case, although the same item of plant may be used for the whole of the work, this might be represented in the bill of quantities by a number of different items, and it is therefore often difficult to price the work as a whole accurately by calculating individual unit rates and adding them together. McCaffer and Baldwin (1984, p. 76) contend that operational estimating is the preferred estimating method for plant-dominated work, and that since heavy civil engineering is plant-dominated it might be expected that operational estimating would be particularly popular for this kind of work.

A building example, quoted in CIOB (1983), is that of a reinforced concrete structure where the cost of placing the concrete may depend not only upon the volume of concrete but also on the type of work involved, including the ratio of formwork, reinforcement and concrete and the total duration of the operation. However, as Harrison (1994) points out:

> …there is no clear dividing line at which operational estimating starts and more usual methods end, the difference being mainly of emphasis and approach…. The appropriateness of operational estimating depends on the nature of the work rather than on the method used to measure it.

Operational estimating techniques therefore involve forecasting the cost of completing an entire construction operation, which may consist of one or more bill items, based upon the resource information generated from the project plan, rather than attempting to forecast the cost of work by formulating separate unit rates for each measured item of work. Operational estimating therefore requires the prior preparation of a method statement, a programme for the work and a resource analysis. The need for a close interaction between estimating and planning is clear, and the whole philosophy is put very succinctly by McCaffer and Baldwin (1984, p. 62):

> If a truly operational estimating approach is adopted then the estimating process comprises planning, calculating the costs of the resources for each operation or activity and transferring these data to the bill of quantities. This approach is popular particularly with companies who have adopted network based planning techniques for most of their contracts.

Harrison, however, also points out that it will usually be desirable, and in some cases essential, for the pricing of some key items to be carried out *alongside* preparation of the resourced programme. The preparation of the programme may well require comparative estimates of cost for alternative methods of construction, and the process of estimating and programming may therefore be an iterative one with a variety of assumptions being made, tested, changed or adopted.

6.2 PREPARATION OF AN OPERATIONAL ESTIMATE: SOME EXAMPLES

The techniques involved in the preparation of operational estimates involve much the same activities as the preparation of unit rates, in that the estimator must include the cost of all of the resources, the labour, plant and materials, required to complete the work within the time allowed by the programme. Preparation of an estimate for a complete operation can therefore, in one sense, be seen as simply a more complex unit rate calculation, but the essential difference is that for an operational estimate the estimator views a section of the work as a whole rather than as a set of separate items.

Table 6.1 shows a typical simple operational calculation for a reinforced concrete wall measured in accordance with the *Standard Method of Measurement of Building Works*, Seventh Edition (SMM7). Although under this method the work falls to be measured as three separate items, the fact that the work is all in one wall means that it makes sense for the estimator to price the work as one complete operation.

As discussed earlier, operational estimating may also be used in the comparison of prices for different methods of executing the same parcel of work. Table 6.2, for example, shows some basic information about a large reinforced concrete tank base, while Tables 6.3 and 6.4 show the detailed price calculations for each of the proposed methods.

Table 6.1 A simple reinforced concrete wall

The following items appear in the concrete work section of a bill of quantities:

In situ reinforced concrete Mix A

Walls; thickness not exceeding 150 mm	6 m^3
Walls; thickness 150–450 mm	9 m^3
Walls; thickness exceeding 450 mm	15 m^3

Method statement

Examination of the drawings shows that the work is all in one continuous wall 30 m long × 4 m high. The concrete is to be placed in a single pour with a mobile crane (already on site) and a concrete skip using ready-mixed concrete delivered in 6 m^3 loads at 1 hour intervals using a 5 man gang.

Rate analysis

Labour

Time allowance		Hours
Preparation time to set up on site	0.50	
Concrete delivery 5 loads × 1 h	5.00	
Clear away on completion	0.50	
		6.00

Gang rate		
Ganger 1 nr @ £7.00/h	7.00	
Concretor 4 nr @ £6.50/h	26.00	
		33.00 per h
		£

Total labour	6 h @ £33.00/h =	198.00

Materials

Ready-mixed concrete 30 m^3 @ £45.00 =		1350.00

Plant

Mobile crane & driver	6 h @ £25.00/h	150.00	
Concrete skip	6 h @ £4.00/h	24.00	
Compressor	6 h @ £5.00/h	30.00	
Vibrator (2 nr)	12 h @ £3.00/h	36.00	240.00
Total cost for 30 m^3			1788.00

Table 6.2 A large reinforced concrete tank base

The following item appears in the concrete work section of a bill of quantities:

> *In situ reinforced concrete Mix A*
>
> Beds; thickness exceeding 450 mm   500 m^3

Examination of the drawings shows that the whole of the work is on one large tank base 20 m × 20 m × 1.25 m thick.

Comparative prices are required for constructing the work:

> 1. Using site-mixed concrete placed over several days with mobile cranes (already on site) including forming construction joints at the end of each day's work
>
> 2. Using ready-mixed concrete placed in one continuous pour with concrete pumps.

6.3   ADVANTAGES AND DISADVANTAGES OF OPERATIONAL ESTIMATING

The advantages of estimating the cost of complete operations, as opposed to preparing unit rate analyses for measured work items, are:

1. When compiling an operational estimate the estimator has a much clearer and more complete picture of the whole task to be done than is usually possible when attempting to build up a price from a unit rate analysis based on measured quantities.

2. Where the work involves extensive use of plant it is often difficult to apportion the costs among a group of measured items. It is for this reason that the operational method is generally preferred for large civil engineering schemes. The use of 'method-related charges' in some civil engineering Standard Methods of Measurement is particularly suited to an operational estimating approach.

3. The estimator may wish to consider the interrelationship of a number of trades or particular combination of resources involved in a particular operation or activity. The use of unit rate methods can mask these interrelationships, but the use of operational methods, in conjunction with the proposed method statement, allows them to be explored in detail. Operational methods also allow easy comparison of alternative methods of carrying out the work.

Table 6.3 Construction using ready-mixed concrete and concrete pumps

Method statement

Total volume of concrete 500 m³. Maximum output per pump using a nine man gang say 21 m³ per hour. One pump will therefore take approximately 24 hours. Use two pumps and complete in 12 hours.

Labour

Time allowance per gang	Hours
Preparation time to set up on site 0.50 h	0.50
Concrete gang 12 h	12.00
Clear away on completion 0.50 h	0.50
Overtime 5.00 h time and a half	2.50
	15.50 h

Concrete gang rate	
Ganger 1 nr @ £7.00/h	7.00
Concretor 8 nr @ £6.50/h	52.00
	59.00/h

Total labour	£
Concrete gang 2 gangs × 15.50 h @ £59.00/h =	1829.00

Materials

Ready-mixed concrete 500 m³ @ £45.00 =	22500.00

Plant

Concrete pump & driver (1 h setup required)		
2 × 13 h @ £30.00/h	780.00	
Overtime say 2 × 4 h @ £8.00/h	64.00	
Compressor 2 × 4 days × @ £5.00/h	40.00	
Vibrator 4 × 12.00 h @ £2.50/h	120.00	1004.00
Total cost for 500 m³		25333.00
Cost/m³ =		£50.61

Table 6.4 Construction using site-mixed concrete and mobile cranes

Method statement

Total volume of concrete 500 m^3. Maximum output per crane using a six man gang say 6 m^3 per hour. One crane will therefore take approximately 83 hours. Use two cranes and complete in 42 hours or 4 working days.

Labour

Time allowance per gang		Hours	
Preparation time to set up 0.50 h/day × 4		2.00	
Concrete gang 4 days × 10.5 h/day		42.00	
Clear away on completion 0.50 h/day × 4		2.00	
Overtime 3.50 h/day × 4 days time and a half		7.00	
			53.00 h
Joiner fix and strip stop ends			
1.50 h/m^2 × 25 m^2/day × 3 days			112.50 h
Concrete gang rate			
Ganger	1 nr @ £7.00/h	7.00	
Concretor	5 nr @ £6.50/h	32.50	
			39.50/h
Total labour		£	
Concrete gang 2 gangs × 53.00 h @ £39.50/h =			4187.00
Joiner 112.50 h @ £7.00 =			787.50
			4,974.50

Materials

Site-mixed concrete 500 m^3 @ £38.00 =		19000.00

Plant

Mobile crane & driver		
2 × 4 days × 10.50 h @ £25.00/h	2100.00	
Overtime say 1.50 h/day × 4 days × 2		
@ £8.00/h	96.00	
Concrete skip 2 × 4 days × 10.50 h @ £4.00/h	336.00	
Compressor 4 days × 10.50 h @ £5.00/h	210.00	
Vibrator 2 × 4 days × 10.50 h @ £2.50/h	210.00	2952.00
Total cost for 500 m^3		26926.50
Cost/m^3 =		£53.85

4. The production rates used in the cost prediction are based upon a carefully prepared programme. The estimate can therefore take account of variations in production rates due to uneconomic or out of sequence working, discontinuous work flow etc.

6.4 CONVERTING THE OPERATIONAL ESTIMATE TO BILL RATES

The usual major disadvantage of operationally generated estimates is in relating the estimate back to measured items of work in the bills of quantities.

Where bills of quantities are provided as part of the tendering documentation quantity surveyors will normally insist that a price is inserted against each and every item in the measured work, but it has long been recognised that bills of quantities produced in the normal 'trade' or 'work section' forms are not generally compatible with operationally produced production information. The difficulty of relating operational estimates to measured items in bills of quantities has historically posed considerable problems for estimators. McCaffer and Baldwin (1984, p. 62), for example, write that '...the major impediment to adopting this (operational) approach is the format of the bill of quantities', while Baxendale (1991) writes that:

> The existing standard methods of measurement were not designed to produce bills of quantities that relate to work items or cost centres. The organisation of construction in the United Kingdom reflects traditional practice and there is inherent resistance to change.

There have been a number of attempts over the past 30 years to find solutions to this problem, perhaps the best known being the various types of operational and activity-based bills pioneered by, among others, the UK Building Research Establishment during the 1960s. The precise methodology proposed is detailed in, for example, Forbes and Skoyles (1963), Skoyles (1964) and Skoyles (1968). The wider implications of the problem have also been clearly recognised for a long time. Nelson (1970), for example, concluded that an operational format for bills of quantities would be much more useful for providing the site with the information it needs. Browning and White (1969), describing an attempt to resolve the problem with a computer system, wrote that:

> Research indicated that many items based on the requirements of the SMM were not ideally suited to modern site production control and site cost feedback. The contractor's estimator, in preparing his estimate for tender, is forced to mirror the work-pieces contained in the bill of quantities. A rift in communication therefore exists between him and the site production staff... the contractor's estimator cannot easily apply

available feed-back of site production experience direct to the pricing, and bills of quantities are not as useful as they should be to the man on site.

Notwithstanding the understanding of the problem, and some initial enthusiasm (e.g. Abbott and Cranswick, 1970), there has been little or no general acceptance, at least on the building side of the industry, of any of the suggested ways to solve it. The only concession seems to have been an attempt in recent years to reduce the number of minor items which used to be measured in the bill. The reasons for the lack of acceptance are perhaps as much to do with the traditional inertia of the construction industry as anything else. According to Willis and Newman (1988, p. 374 *et seq.*):

> This reluctance [to accept operational bills] probably stems from the architects' resistance to produce operational drawings, the quantity surveyors' lack of expertise in preparing building programmes and the estimators' need to change radically the estimating process. Difficulty was also experienced in the valuing of work varied during the contract which often had to be done by negotiation. This bill format can obviously be described as a progressive and worthwhile innovation, but it probably came at a time when the industry was too busy and traditionally resistant to change....

It does not, at first sight, seem fair to accuse estimators of being unwilling to change their processes. It is after all common for estimators to price parcels of work on an operational basis, particularly for projects let on a design and build or plan and specification basis where the contractor has to prepare its own quantities. It may be, however, that estimators' willingness to try operational methods may not be universal. Mueller (1986) for example, while arguing for the adoption of operational techniques by construction estimators in the USA, writes that:

> Estimating is customarily done by trade groupings following some standardised job cost chart of accounts. Indeed, embedded in the industry is a mindset towards estimating by trade groupings and summarisation by common work types. By comparison estimating by activity requires advanced preparation of the roster of activities....

It is undoubtedly true that the use of operational techniques makes the valuation of variations more difficult, in that it is no longer possible simply to use unit rates from the bills of quantities. This might, however, from the contractors' point of view, be considered a distinct advantage, since there has long been a view that the use of bill rates has frequently meant that contractors have received a less than economic price for varied work.

Perhaps the most significant objection to the production of operational bills by quantity surveyors is that operational estimating is not seen as a substitute for unit rate estimating but a complement to it. According to Harrison (1994):

> ...the unit rate and operational estimating approaches are complementary and there are many circumstances in which a combination will be appropriate. This could be at job level with some items priced by each method, or at item level with both methods used in pricing a single item. The labour and plant elements might be dealt with by operational estimating and the materials and subcontractors on an item by item basis.

The difficulties quantity surveyors would face in preparing a tender document for a project which contractors might want to price in this way, and what is more where every tendering contractor might want to price the items using different combinations of methods, is obvious.

Where the operation relates only to a single bill item there is obviously no problem in relating the operational costs back to bill items, but the following are four suggested ways (Harrison, 1994) in which operational estimates can be related back to ranges of 'traditional' measured items such as that illustrated in Table 6.1:

1. Calculate comparative rates for operations on an operational and an individual unit rate basis. Price the items in the bill using the unit rates and 'lose' the difference between the unit rate and operational estimates in the Preliminaries section.

2. Divide the total operational cost by the total quantity of all of the items to give an average rate. In the case of the example quoted in Table 6.1, each of the three items would be priced at a rate of £59.60.

3. The average rate method described above takes no account of the relative difficulty of carrying out the various items of work. Where this is considered to be important, for example where it is believed that the quantities may be substantially varied in the course of the work, then an average weighted price can be calculated. In this case the billed quantity of each item is weighted to reflect the comparative difficulty, and the total operation price is divided by the total weighted quantity. The unit rate for each item is then the unit price multiplied by the appropriate weighting. In the case of the example shown in Table 6.1 the calculations are as follows:

Walls thickness not exceeding 150 mm	$6 \text{ m}^3 \times$ weighting 2.5 =	15
Walls thickness 150–450 mm	$9 \text{ m}^3 \times$ weighting 2 =	18
Walls thickness exceeding 450 mm	$15 \text{ m}^3 \times$ weighting 1 =	<u>15</u>
	Total weighted quantity	<u>48 m^3</u>

Unit rate = £1788 ÷ 48 = <u>£37.25</u>

Weighted unit rates are therefore as follows:

Walls thickness not exceeding 150 mm	£37.25 × weighting 2.5 =	£93.13
Walls thickness 150–450 mm	£37.25 × weighting 2 =	£74.50
Walls thickness not exceeding 450 mm	£37.25 × weighting 1 =	£37.25

The priced bill of quantities is therefore:

Walls thickness not exceeding 150 mm	6 m^3	£93.13	558.78
Walls thickness 150–450 mm	9 m^3	£74.50	670.50
Walls thickness not exceeding 450 mm	15 m^3	£37.25	558.75
			1788.03

4. Unit rates for each billed item are calculated in the usual way and summed to give a total cost. This is then compared with the total cost calculated using operational techniques, and the difference between the two figures is then allocated to each bill item on a proportional basis. The following example, again based on Table 6.1, gives the general idea.

Assume that the straightforward unit rate calculations give the following rates:

Walls thickness not exceeding 150 mm	6 m^3	£80.50	483.00
Walls thickness 150–450 mm	9 m^3	£75.00	675.00
Walls thickness exceeding 450 mm	15 m^3	£35.00	525.00
			1683.00

This compares with a price of £1788.00 from the operational estimate, and the calculation to spread this difference over the unit rates is as follows:

Walls thickness not exceeding 150 mm		
£80.50 × 1788 ÷ 1683 =	£85.52 × 6 m^3 =	513.12
Walls thickness 150–450 mm		
£75.00 × 1788 ÷ 1683 =	£79.68 × 9 m^3 =	717.12
Walls thickness exceeding 450 mm		
£35.00 × 1788 ÷ 1683 =	£37.18 × 15 m^3 =	557.70
		1,787.94

6.5 METHOD-RELATED CHARGES

Some of these issues were at least partially addressed by the Institution of Civil Engineers in the second edition of the Civil Engineering Standard Method of Measurement (CESMM2) with the introduction of method-related charges, which allow tendering contractors to define groups of items in the bill, and to insert charges against these groups of items to reflect the direct costs of carrying out the work by specific methods where the cost is not proportional to the quantity of the work. These charges may themselves be subdivided to

Table 6.5 Example of method-related charges

Number	Description	Unit	Quantity	Rate	Amount
	<u>Method-related charges</u>				
	Plant				
	Plant for concreting main bridge piers				
	Concrete pumps – 2 nr				
A340.1	*Bring to site; Fixed charge*	*Sum*			
A340.2	*Operate; Time-related charge*	*Sum*			
A340.3	*Remove; Fixed charge*	*Sum*			
	20 tn mobile crane				
A341.1	*Bring to site; Fixed charge*	*Sum*			
A341.2	*Operate; Time-related charge*	*Sum*			
A341.3	*Remove; Fixed charge*	*Sum*			
	Erection of falsework to main bridge deck; Fixed charge				
A350.1	*Bridge A*	*Sum*			_____
	Page nr 1/10		Page total		

show recurrent or time-related costs, such as the maintenance of site facilities, and also those lump sum costs which are neither time- nor quantity-related, such as setting up and dismantling major pieces of plant or constructing temporary site access roads. Barnes (1986, p. 73) sums up the idea:

> In commissioning civil engineering work the Employer buys the materials left behind, but only hires from the Contractor the men and machines which manipulate them, and the management skill to manipulate them effectively. It is logical to assess their values in the same terms as the origin of their costs. It is illogical not to do so if the Employer is to retain the right at any time to vary what is left behind and if the financial uncertainties affecting Employer and Contractor are to be minimised.

Table 6.5 shows a typical extract from the method-related charges section of a bill of quantities, but McCaffer and Baldwin (1984, p. 62) make the point that although the introduction of method-related charges encourages the concepts of operational estimating, the Civil Engineering Standard Method of Measurement does not produce operational bills. It is also claimed (McGowan *et al.*, 1994) that the adoption of method-related charges has not been widespread, perhaps due to contractors' unwillingness to 'show their hand'. Further information on the use of method-related charges is given in Seeley (1993).

The issue of pricing time-related and non-time-related items is considered further in Chapter 8.

6.6   REFERENCES

Abbott B. and Cranswick R. (1970) 'Operational bills: users' comments', *Architect's Journal*, 11 March 1970, pp. 617–20.

Barnes M. (1986) *The CESMM2 Handbook*, Thomas Telford, London.

Baxendale A.T. (1991) 'Management information systems: the use of work breakdown structure in the integration of time and cost', in *Management, Quality and Economics of Building* (eds. Bezalga A. and Brandon P.), E. & F.N. Spon, London.

Browning C.D. and White P.D. (1969) 'Link computer system', *Building*, 10 October 1969, pp. 89–90.

CIOB (1983) *Code of Estimating Practice*, Chartered Institute of Building, London.

Forbes W.S. and Skoyles E.R (1963) 'The operational bill', *The Chartered Surveyor*, Vol. 95, pp. 429–34, Royal Institution of Chartered Surveyors, London.

Harrison R.S. (1994) *Operational estimating*, CIOB Construction Papers No. 33, Chartered Institute of Building, London.

McCaffer R. and Baldwin A. (1984) *Estimating and Tendering for Civil Engineering Works*, Granada Technical Books, London.

McGowan P.H., Malcolm R., Horner W., Jones D. and Thompson P. (1994) *Allocation and evaluation of risk in construction contracts*, Occasional Paper No. 52, Chartered Institute of Building, London.

Mueller F.W. (1986) *Integrated Cost and Schedule Control for Construction Projects*, Van Nostrand Reinhold, New York.

Nelson J.I'A. (1970) 'Construction Information', *Building Technology and Management*, Vol. 8, pp. 3–5.

Skoyles E.R. (1964) 'Introduction to Operational Bills. Building Research Station Design Series 32', *The Quantity Surveyor*, Vol. 21, No. 2, pp. 27–32.

Skoyles E.R. (1968) *Introducing Bill of Quantities (Operational Format)*, BRS current paper CP62/68, Building Research Establishment, London.

Willis C.J. and Newman D. (1988) *Elements of Quantity Surveying*, 8th edn, BSP Professional Books, Oxford.

7 Subcontractors

7.1 INTRODUCTION

[The construction of modern buildings is an extremely complex process, and the modern construction industry is increasingly characterised by a greater and greater degree of specialisation. It is therefore highly unlikely that any one main contractor will have either the necessary skills or the necessary resources to do all of the work on a project itself, and it is common for sections of the work to be sublet to other specialists.]

[The degree of subcontracting will vary greatly from project to project depending upon factors such as the project type, size, complexity and time-scale, and also depending upon the subcontracting policy of each individual main contractor.]Some, particularly perhaps the old established 'traditional' firms, will tend to employ a nucleus of key craft operatives directly, subcontracting where necessary to supplement their own resources and expertise, whereas other firms exist as almost pure management organisations, concentrating solely on providing overall organisation and management skills and subcontracting virtually the whole of the actual construction. But whatever the circumstances of any particular project it is likely that a substantial proportion of the work, almost certainly in excess of 50%, will be carried out by subcontractors of one kind or another, and it is therefore essential for estimators to have a detailed knowledge of the factors which govern the incorporation of subcontractors' prices into the main contractor's estimate.

This chapter therefore considers:

1. The various types of subcontractor

2. The advantages and disadvantages to the main contractor of subletting work to others

3. The process of obtaining subcontractors' prices

4. The contractual relationships between the various types of subcontractor, the main contractor and the client

81

5. Incorporation of subcontractors' prices into the main project estimate

6. Negotiation with subcontractors

7.2   TYPES OF SUBCONTRACTOR

Several types of subcontractor are common in construction work, over each of which the main contractor exercises varying degrees of control, and to each of which it owes varying degrees of responsibility. Each of the main types is described separately below. Note, however, that normally the main contractor has overall and complete responsibility to the client for ensuring that the project as a whole is constructed in accordance with the contract. It will therefore be held responsible to the client for ensuring that subcontractors complete their work to the quality standards laid down in the contract documents. The main contractor is also responsible for the organisation and management of the works and the site, and will therefore also be responsible for integrating the various subcontract works into the overall project pro-gramme, and for ensuring that the subcontractors comply with any relevant statutory requirements such as health and safety legislation.

Detailed consideration of the various contractual relationships and pricing factors which the estimator will need to consider are each discussed in detail later.

7.2.1   Nominated Subcontractors

Nominated subcontractors are usually defined as 'persons whose final selec-tion and approval for the supply and fixing of any materials or goods or the execution of any work has been reserved to the architect'. Nominated subcontractors are therefore chosen by the architect to carry out specific parts of the project. Hughes (1992) lists a number of reasons why architects or employers might want to do this. Perhaps the most important are where particular and specialised equipment has to be installed by a particular firm, and where lead times for the manufacture of specialised equipment mean that orders must be placed in advance of the main contract tender period.

The detailed procedures to be followed vary from one standard form of contract to another, and will be considered later, but in essence tenders for nominated subcontract work will be invited by the architect, who will then select which firm will do the work. The main contractor will then be instructed to enter into a subcontract with the chosen firm.

Allowances for nominated subcontractors' work will normally be included in the bills of quantities as a prime cost sum. Supplementary items will be included for the main contractor to include allowances for profit, general and special attendance.

7.2.2 Named Subcontractors

The term 'named subcontractors' is specifically used here to refer to subcontractors chosen by the architect but where full nomination is not appropriate. The most common use of this type of subcontractor in the UK is where the project is let under the JCT Intermediate Form of Contract (JCT84), which has no provision for nominated subcontractors. In this case the procedure is for the architect to invite tenders from chosen subcontractors using a special tender form and, as in the case of nomination, the main contractor is then required to enter into a contract with the chosen firm.

Since the forms of contract using this technique have no provision for nomination, the work cannot be included in the bill of quantities as a prime cost sum. In those cases where the subcontractor has not been chosen at the time of the main contract tender the work will normally be covered by a provisional sum in the tender documents. On the other hand, if the architect has already chosen the subcontractor prior to the preparation of the main contract estimate, then the tendering contractors will be given the chosen subcontractor's tender and required to include it in the main contract tender for the work. The main contractor is therefore free to make whatever additions it wishes to the subcontractor's price to cover profit, general and special attendance, and the named subcontractor becomes contractually, in effect, a domestic subcontractor. Massey (1992), however, makes the point that although the position of the named subcontractor is similar to that of a domestic subcontractor, there are in fact subtle practical differences, since, in the case of the named subcontractor the main contractor does not have control of the process of inviting tenders and therefore has no scope for price negotiation.

Note that subcontractors are often 'named' in another sense in bills of quantities, where the main contractor is typically given a list of firms from which it must choose one to carry out some particular part of the work. A typical case might be where some particular material has to be fixed by a specialist approved by the material supplier. In this case final choice of the specific subcontractor to be used for the work is left to the main contractor provided that the firm chosen appears on the given list. In many, perhaps most, cases the tendering contractors will be given the right to suggest alternative firms of their own choice subject to the approval of the architect. Even though the contractor's choice may be restricted therefore, subcontractors of this type are still classified as 'domestic'.

7.2.3 Domestic Subcontractors

Virtually all standard forms of contract permit the main contractor to sublet portions of the work to firms of its own choosing provided that certain conditions are met. Subcontractors chosen in this way are termed 'domestic' subcontractors.

The restrictions imposed on the main contractor vary from one standard form to another, but the simplest is the JCT Minor Works Agreement, clause 3.2 of which simply states that:

> The contractor shall not subcontract the works or any part thereof without the written consent of the Architect whose consent shall not unreasonably be withheld.

Similar provisions are included in other forms, but are supplemented by a variety of additional stipulations about the terms of the subcontract, essentially to ensure that, if the main contract is determined, then the subcontracts are also determined, and also to ensure that title to any unfixed goods and materials on the site passes to the employer as soon as the main contractor has been paid for them. Note, however, that while the various JCT forms of contract state that although the architect's permission to sublet is required, this shall not be unreasonably withheld; under the UK Government GC/Wks/1 form the supervising officer's powers of refusal of any proposed subcontractor are absolute.

Domestic subcontractors are commonly divided into two basic types:

> 1. Subcontractors carrying out complete parcels of work including providing all of the necessary labour, plant and materials. Examples might be piling, plumbing installations or the fabrication and erection of structural steelwork.

> 2. Labour-only subcontractors, where all of the necessary materials and plant are provided by the main contractor. Examples might be a bricklaying gang or a concreting gang.

Brook (1993, p. 95), however, identifies a third classification, where the subcontractor provides labour and plant, with any materials being provided by the main contractor. This arrangement may have some advantages in cases where the work requires specialised plant but the main contractor wishes to exercise tight control of materials purchasing and supply.

7.3   ADVANTAGES AND DISADVANTAGES TO THE MAIN CONTRACTOR

Although the main contractor has little or no choice in the case of 'nominated' and 'named' subcontractors, the use of domestic subcontractors is almost entirely at its discretion, subject to any necessary approvals being obtained from the architect or engineer. It is therefore pertinent to look briefly at some of the principal advantages and disadvantages to the main contractor of subletting parts of the work.

There are basically four major reasons why a main contractor will look to subcontract parts of the work:

1. It may be unhappy about the degree of risk involved in some element of the works, and may simply seek to reduce or eliminate that risk by shifting it in whole or in part to someone else. The issue of risk assessment and analysis as it affects the estimating and tendering process is considered in detail in Chapter 12.

2. To supplement its existing resources in order either to achieve the required time-scale or to allow its own resources to be used on other projects.

3. To remove the need for it to provide a constant flow of work for its own employees. Once a contractor employs workers on a permanent basis it must then obtain a regular and reasonably smooth flow of work in order to keep them fully employed. This may be difficult in some trades. It would, for example, nowadays normally be considered uneconomic for a main contractor to employ its own glaziers or plasterers, and there is therefore a tendency for trades of this type to be subcontracted.

4. Particular parts of the work, may be of a specialised nature, for example piling or the erection of structural steelwork. In these cases the main contractor may not possess either the necessary specialist skills or equipment, and it will therefore need to hire them in.

The major disadvantage of subletting the work from the main contractor's point of view is one of coordination and control. Remember that, as far as the client and the architect are concerned, any domestic subcontract is a purely private matter between the main contractor and the subcontractor, and the main contractor carries full responsibility for satisfactory completion of the whole of the works. Quality and time control of domestic subcontractors, particularly where they have submitted a keen price, is obviously much more difficult for the contractor than it would be if it were carrying out the work using its own resources. In addition, one must also consider the possibility that subcontractors may themselves decide to sublet parts of the their own subcontract to sub-subcontractors. In some parts of the world, for example in Hong Kong, the construction industry is characterised by multiple levels of subcontracting, such that almost every person employed on the work is self-employed. Subcontracting means that main contractors no longer have total control of the resources required to complete the work, and the more extensive the subcontracting becomes the greater the difficulty the main contractor is likely to have in retaining a sufficient degree of control of the project as a whole.

A further financial disadvantage is that subletting the work may reduce the contractor's profit-making opportunities. The total amount of profit which can be added to the net cost of any project is limited, largely by market factors, and since the subcontractors will obviously also look to make a profit from their resources the main contractor's profit margin must inevitably be reduced. Adrian (1982, pp. 157–8), makes the point well:

> Typically the competitive nature of the construction industry does not permit the general contractor to mark up subcontractors' work at the same rate he marks up his own work…. In effect, given the competitiveness of the construction industry, the more a general contractor subcontracts work, the less he can mark up the subcontract work in the interests of preparing a competitive bid.

7.4   SUBCONTRACT ENQUIRIES

It has already been shown that, for most projects, subcontracted work will comprise a high proportion of the total project estimate. Remember also that, if the contractor's tender is accepted, its tender estimate will become the budget for the work, and it will therefore be heavily reliant on the satisfactory performance of its subcontractors to complete the work within the required time, quality and budgetary constraints. It is therefore in the contractor's interest to ensure that the prices it receives from its domestic subcontractors are as accurate as possible and are truly representative of the work to be done, and the first step to ensuring that this is the case is to make sure that all subcontractors receive accurate and complete information. In the words of the CIOB Code of Estimating Practice (CIOB, 1983, p. 47):

> The objective of sending out enquiries is to produce technically accurate quotations and to set out clearly the terms and conditions on which quotations are being invited.

In the case of nominated and named subcontractors the invitation of prices will be dealt with by the architect, and the contractor's involvement in the process will be limited to settling details such as interfacing the subcontractors' time requirements with the main project programme. In the case of domestic subcontractors, however, the provision of the necessary information will be entirely the main contractor's responsibility. In essence the subcontractor needs precisely as much information about the subcontract works as the main contractor itself needs to compile its own estimate. Enquiries must therefore include:

1. Basic project details, such as the location of the works, names of the employer and consultants, details of the main and subcontracts to be used, details shown in the Appendix to the main contract, whether a fixed or fluctuating price is required and where further drawings may be inspected.

2. A general description of the subcontract works, complete with information on access, any noise restrictions, police regulations etc.

3. Details of any general attendance, services and facilities which will be available for the subcontractors' use, such as standing scaffolding, mess rooms, latrines, materials storage etc.

4. Main and subcontract programme, method statement and details of any phasing requirements

5. Extracts from the measured work included in the bills of quantities, relevant specification and preliminaries information and all necessary drawings and schedules.

6. The date quotations are to be returned and any discounts required.

It is important that the estimator maintains a register of subcontract enquiries and tenders. The precise form, together with the procedures to be used should form part of the company's quality assurance manual, and CIOB (1983) also includes examples of good practice.

A further question to be considered is which subcontractors should be invited to submit prices for the work. In many cases the contractor is likely to have a pool of subcontractors with which it works on a regular basis. Well-organised contractors will maintain records of subcontractors, including the projects for which they were used, their success or otherwise in meeting the required standards and any difficulties experienced. In the case of large subcontracts main contractors may wish to select a list of suitable firms through the same kind of pre-qualification process as a client might use for the main contract (see Chapter 14).

Responsibility for procuring subcontractors' quotations will vary from firm to firm. In some cases the work will be done by the estimator, but in larger firms the process may be undertaken by a buyer, who will simply present the subcontractors' prices to the estimator for inclusion in the estimate.

7.5 CONTRACTUAL RELATIONSHIPS

7.5.1 Nominated Subcontractors

In the case of subcontractors nominated under the provisions of any of the standard forms of construction contract the various contractual relationships between the main contractor, subcontractors and the employer are defined clearly in the contract documentation. Standard forms generally exist for the invitation of subcontract tenders and for the subcontract between the main contractor and the nominated subcontractor. The detailed provisions, however, differ between the various standard forms of contract.

The nomination of subcontractors can give rise to some complex problems, particularly where the subcontract works include an element of design, for example piling or the provision of a precast reinforced concrete frame, where the employer may look for some form of protection from the designer in the form of a warranty. In addition the subcontract documentation must take account of the fact that although the original offer is made to the architect as agent of the employer, acceptance of the offer and the execution of the subcontract is a matter for the main contractor. The standard documentation attempts to take account of these problems.

The most complex procedures are probably those included in the 1980 edition of the United Kingdom Standard Form of Building Contract (JCT80). In this case the architect invites tenders for the work using the standard tender form, but before the tender can be accepted the main contractor and subcontractor have to agree details of the programme. Only after the programme details are agreed can the architect instruct the main contractor to enter into the appropriate subcontract. The question of a warranty for design work is covered with yet another standard form which is signed between the subcontractor and the employer. These arrangements are very complex and the procedure is very long-winded. The procedure has been heavily criticised for being very time-consuming, but it does at least try to ensure that the most contentious problems are solved before the subcontract is signed. Particular criticism was, however, voiced by the respected lawyer and author I.N. Duncan Wallace (Wallace, 1986, p. 536) when he wrote that:

> ...the 1980 JCT contract has embarked on yet a new nomination procedure, complicated to the point of impracticality from an administrative point of view.... The main and most important result... is to create a bewildering and extraordinarily complicated series of interlocking triangular liabilities as between employer, main contractor and nominated subcontractors. The resulting problems... can be expected to occupy the appellate courts in the United Kingdom for years to come.

The Joint Contracts Tribunal attempted to reduce the complexity of the original arrangements in 1991 with the publication of the tenth amendment to the JCT80 contract. This amendment replaced the original four standard documents with seven new ones, but the contractual relationships are unaffected.

Wallace also considers the JCT nomination procedure to be inferior to what he calls the stark simplicity of that included in the GC/Wks/1 form, where there is a simple chain of responsibility and the main contractor is responsible to the employer for the performance of subcontractors.

In addition, some conditions of contract make provision for main contractors to receive discounts from nominated subcontractors and nominated suppliers provided that payments are made within the terms of the contract (JCT80 is typical, with nominated subcontractors required to allow a 2.5% discount and nominated suppliers required to allow 5%). Contractors' attitudes towards these discounts will vary. Those contractors who intend to honour the subcontract payment provisions in the Conditions of Contract may treat discounts as a contribution to profit, and adjust their tender figures accordingly, but other contractors may choose to ignore them on the basis that they can improve their own cash flow position relatively cheaply by sacrificing the discounts in favour of late payment of subcontractors and suppliers.

7.5.2 Named Subcontractors

It has already been shown that there is no provision for nomination in the IFC84 form, and the position of named subcontractors is therefore very similar to domestic subcontractors. The IFC84 documentation does, however, include a procedure and standard forms for the invitation of tenders from named subcontractors, and a set of subcontract conditions which set out the respective rights and liabilities of the main contractor and named subcontractors.

7.5.3 Domestic Subcontractors

Although in general terms the agreement of subcontract conditions between the main contractor and its domestic subcontractors is a totally private matter, many of the standard forms of contract do provide optional agreements for use in this situation. The JCT80 form for example has form DOM/1, and the JCT form for use with contractor's design (CD1981) has form DOM/2, which also allows for the passing of design liability where design is to be carried out by the subcontractor. The usage of these forms is not, however, mandatory, and there is nothing to prevent main contractors using their own forms if they so wish. The imposition of unfair conditions by main contractors (an example is the notorious 'pay when paid' clause, where subcontractors are not paid until the main contractor has been paid) has long been a problem for domestic subcontractors. Nicholls (1993), while discussing the latest UK Government attempts to reduce conflict in the construction industry, sees the issue in wider terms than simply the main contractor/subcontractor relationship:

Far from being seen as an instrument to prevent or resolve conflict, contracts have increasingly become a way in which dispute is deliberately fomented to provide leverage on price. The distortion and discounting of Standard Forms of Main Contracts has encouraged contractors, generally, to ignore the terms of agreed standard subcontracts and to replace them with a proliferation of home-spun subcontracts, or to mutilate the standard forms of subcontract to such a degree that they become virtually unrecognisable.

There is therefore no set procedure for establishing a domestic subcontract. Indeed, in some cases, particularly in the case of labour-only subcontractors, the contract may not even be in writing. This is not good practice. All contracts should, wherever possible, be in writing (at least an exchange of letters) in case disputes subsequently occur.

7.6   SETTLING THE SUBCONTRACT PRICE

All subcontract prices should be carefully checked on receipt to ensure arithmetical accuracy, that they are in accordance with the contract conditions and the main contractor's requirements, that every item is priced consistently and realistically, and that they include all of the necessary information for the estimator to make the necessary comparisons and analysis. It is most important that the estimator is able to compare the prices with each other on an equal basis. Table 7.1 shows a typical selection from subcontractors' tenders for the floor finishes element. It is plain that the lowest price has been submitted by Bloggs Bros., but examination of their rates shows a significant difference between their price for item 4/1/c and those submitted by all of the other tenderers. It would appear at least likely that this might be an error, and the estimator must therefore check with the lowest tenderer and be sure that the rates are realistic before accepting the lowest tender.

Computer software can make the process of comparison and analysis much easier. In the absence of anything more sophisticated a simple spreadsheet such as that used for Table 7.1 will prove very useful.

Having compared the rates the estimator must also look for any changes which the subcontractors may have made to the contract conditions. Unacceptable conditions included by the subcontractors may need to be the subject of negotiation, but it may not be possible for the negotiations to be completed in time for submission of the estimate. In this case the estimator may have to make an assessment of the cost of removing unacceptable conditions and adjust the subcontract price accordingly. In the words of Massey (1992):

This may well mean that subcontract prices received during the tender period are often no more than an indicator and in order to arrive at a considered net cost, account must be taken of these anomalies and their financial effect.

Table 7.1 Comparison of subcontract tenders

Floor finishings

Bill item	Quantity	Jones & Son		Bloggs Bros.		Bodgit Ltd		Smith & Co.	
		Rate	Extension	Rate	Extension	Rate	Extension	Rate	Extension
4/1/a	750 m^2	1.25	937.50	1.20	900.00	1.57	1177.50	1.62	1215.00
4/1/b	433 m^2	2.22	961.26	2.00	866.00	2.00	866.00	2.30	995.90
4/1/c	102 m^2	6.23	635.46	3.18	324.36	6.50	663.00	6.19	631.38
4/1/d	300 m^2	5.55	1665.00	5.60	1680.00	5.36	1608.00	5.40	1620.00
4/1/e	288 m^2	5.45	1569.60	5.95	1713.60	5.45	1569.60	5.52	1589.76
4/2/a	345 m^2	4.67	1611.15	4.80	1656.00	4.75	1638.75	4.86	1676.70
4/2/b	1023 m	0.12	122.76	0.15	153.45	0.11	112.53	0.40	409.20
4/2/c	346 m	1.35	467.10	1.20	415.20	1.45	501.70	1.00	346.00
Total of quotation £			7969.83		7708.61		8137.08		8483.94

This leads to the view that the subcontractors submitting the lowest price in response to the initial tender enquiry may not be the ones who eventually do the work. Massey also makes the point that:

> ...the contractor can (and often does) obtain further domestic subcon-tract prices after his own tender has been submitted. Often these prices will reflect different values than those obtained during the tender period.... Given the foregoing, the prices obtained from subcontractors during the tender period are not always those upon which the eventual subcontract will be placed. The subcontract will often be placed at a lower price.

Some American commentators expressly advocate that contractors should capitalise on this situation by negotiating with those subcontractors who have not submitted the lowest price in an attempt to drive the price down further. This process, called 'bid peddling' or 'bid shopping', is deemed unethical by the American Society of Professional Estimators. Canon #7 of their Code of Professional Ethics says that:

> Professional estimators shall not engage in the practice of 'bid peddling' as defined by this code. This is a breach of moral and ethical standards and this practice shall not be entered into by a member of the society.

Nonetheless, Ayres (1984, pp. 21–2) for example writes that:

> It is in the period between the time the general contractor is selected and the time the contract is signed that bid peddling takes place. By 'bid peddling' we mean that the general contractor calls subcontractors other than the low bidder for each trade; the low figure may or may not be revealed, but all subcontractors are asked to reduce their price. Each subcontractor is played against the others until the lowest possible price is obtained.

Diamant (1988, p. 47) goes even further:

> When they [subcontractors] know that you are serious about the bid and you are truly looking for the lowest price they will sharpen their pencils. This of course involves true negotiations working one contractor against another to solicit the best price. By true negotiation it is possible to work with the contractor who may need this job more than the next. He may be willing to cut his mark-up. Another contractor may see the job in a more economical way.

Hinze and Tracey (1994), reporting an American survey of subcontractors' views of the general contractor/subcontractor relationship confirm that bid shopping is still apparently prevalent in the USA. In a study of 28 subcontract firms spanning a range of specialisms, three-quarters of the sample stated that they knew of projects for which they had submitted the lowest bids but had not secured the work. Hinze and Tracey also make the point that it is not only the main contractor who engages in bid shopping:

> [bid shopping] is typically initiated by a subcontractor. Basically this occurs when a subcontractor obtains specific information about the lowest amount that has been bid by the competing subcontractors. A subcontractor who initiates bid shopping... must identify a general contractor who is willing to disclose the bids of other subcontractors or at least give some indication of the relative standing of the enquiring subcontractor's bid. If the bid is not the lowest bid, the subcontractor must then assess the merits of submitting a reduced bid. Although the practice is widely regarded as unethical pre-bid bid shopping does appear to occur with some frequency...

Runeson (1988) confirms that similar problems occur in Australia. Reporting on earlier surveys (Uher and Runeson, 1984, 1985) he writes that out of 41 general contractors surveyed only 13 habitually selected the lowest subcontract bid, while 27 admitted to engaging in bid shopping and 35 contractors admitted to using the lowest bid as a basis for negotiation with other subcontractors. On the other hand, out of 43 subcontractors 22 varied their bids to different contractors and 21 admitted making allowances in their bids for anticipated negotiations.

Klein (1994) complains vehemently about the high incidence of bid peddling in the UK:

> The most usual complaint is about Dutch auctioning or bid peddling.... Both pre-tender and post-tender there are frequent rounds of bidding amongst subcontractors, including those not involved in the initial tender exercise.

Klein also documents other recent causes of subcontractors' complaints including:

Poorly prepared tender documentation that makes pricing impossible

Non-standard questionnaires for pre-qualification and qualification

Non-standard contract documents or amended standard forms

Lengthy tender lists

Inadequate tendering times

Charges for inclusion on tender lists

Selection criteria that are not always fairly applied across the board

7.7   INCORPORATION OF DOMESTIC SUBCONTRACTORS' PRICES INTO THE MAIN PROJECT ESTIMATE

The method of incorporating domestic and 'named' subcontractors' prices into the main contractor's estimate will vary depending upon the tender documentation and the work included in the subcontract. In the case of work let on bills of quantities, subcontractors' prices have to be related to items in the bill. It is not uncommon for estimators to try to include a lump sum price for a range of items in the bill, but the quantity surveyor will almost always ask for this to be broken down into rates for individual items.

Where the subcontract includes labour, materials and plant, the estimator merely will often simply insert the rates from the subcontract tender plus any addition for profit and overheads where a 'gross' pricing approach is being used. Where the subcontract simply includes labour and plant, the estimator must of course add the appropriate material costs to the subcontractor's price.

In the case of labour-only subcontractors it is likely that the price quoted will not relate to bill items and the estimator must then allocate the subcontract price to the appropriate bill items. As an example, consider a labour-only bricklaying subcontract where the subcontract will often be based on something like a rate per 1000 bricks laid. In this case the estimator must consider how this can be related to the bill items which are generally measured by area. The easiest method is shown in Table 7.2. Similar techniques can be used in other trades.

7.8   ATTENDANCES

All subcontractors will expect that some basic facilities will be provided by the main contractor. Specific requirements will vary from case to case, and such facilities are termed 'attendance'. Attendances are usually subdivided into 'general' attendance and 'special' attendance. General attendance relates to those general 'site infrastructure' facilities, such as temporary roads, temporary services, safety, health and welfare facilities, which the main contractor, in its position of construction team leader, would have to provide for its own use and which it would be impractical to expect each of the subcontractors to provide for themselves. General attendance on nominated subcontractors is defined in the *Standard Method of Measurement of Building*

Table 7.2 Conversion of rates per 1000 to costs per m²

Labour only subcontract price: £210 per 1000 bricks laid including sundry labours

Cost per m² for any wall thickness is therefore:

$$\frac{\text{Cost per 1000 bricks}}{1000} \times \text{number of bricks per m}^2$$

Costs m² for various wall thicknesses are therefore:

Wall thickness	Bricks/m²	Laying cost
Half brick	60	£12.60
One brick	120	£25.20
One and a half bricks	180	£37.80
Two bricks	240	£50.40

Works: Seventh Edition (SMM7) as being deemed to include (Section A clause A42.1.16 and coverage rule C3):

> ...the use of the Contractor's temporary roads, pavings and paths, standing scaffolding, standing power operated hoisting plant, the provision of temporary lighting and water supplies, clearing away rubbish, provision of space for subcontractors' own offices and the storage of his plant and materials and the use of mess-rooms, sanitary accommodation and welfare facilities provided by the Contractor.

Seeley (1989) provides more information on the contractor's general items, and their costing is covered in Chapter 8.

It is also likely that contractors will normally make these facilities available to their own domestic subcontractors. Pricing of these items will be included in the preliminaries element, and they will usually be priced by reference to the master programme. The pricing of preliminaries is considered in more detail in Chapter 8.

Special attendance refers to items which the main contractor is required to provide for the individual use of specific subcontractors. A typical example is shown in Table 7.3.

Pricing of items such as this follows closely the pricing of many preliminaries items in that the cost is partially fixed (i.e. the cost of establishing the hardstanding and its subsequent removal) and partially time-related (i.e. maintenance of the hardstanding for the period it is required). The item is therefore very similar to the temporary access road shown in Chapter 8.

Table 7.3 Prime cost sums for nominated subcontractors

Prime cost sums		
Include the Prime Cost Sum of £100 000.00 for the supply and erection of structural steelwork as generally shown on drawing Nos. 1234/SL(2)100, 101 and 102		£100 000.00
Add for profit	%	
Add for general attendance	Item	
Add for special attendance as follows:		
Hardstanding adjacent to the working area including access suitable for vehicles of 32 tonnes gross weight	Item	

Although in the above discussion attendances have been subdivided between general and special attendance and the assumption has been made that
they will be priced separately this may not always be the case. There may be
occasions where the same or similar items of special attendance are required
for a number of different subcontractors, and it may therefore be convenient
to schedule all attendances required for the whole project and consider them
all together. Massey (1992) is quite unequivocal, writing that:

> It is believed that ALL attendances for ALL subcontractors should be
> considered collectively unless they can be specifically identified as being
> applicable to one subcontract and can be priced as such.

7.9   CONCLUSION

In conclusion, it must be remembered that in the modern construction
industry the main contractor cannot survive without subcontractors. The
industry is now so specialised and projects so complex that no main contractor
can undertake the whole project on its own. Main contractors depend on their
subcontractors for their very survival in business, and a good relationship with
all types of subcontractor is therefore essential. That relationship starts at the
tender stage, and good management of the subcontract tendering process will
help to maximise the chances of a successful outcome from both parties'
points of view.

Readers requiring more detailed information on the financial and operational aspects of subcontracting under the JCT Standard Forms of Building
Contract are referred to Price (1994).

7.10 REFERENCES

Adrian J.J.A. (1982) *Construction estimating*, Reston Publishing Company, Reston VA.

Ayres C. (1984) *Specifications for Architecture, Engineering and Construction*, 2nd edn, McGraw-Hill, New York.

Brook M. (1993) *Estimating and Tendering for Construction Work*, Butterworth-Heinemann, Oxford.

CIOB (1983) *Code of Estimating Practice*, 5th edn, Chartered Institute of Building, London.

Diamant L. (1988) *Construction Estimating for General Contractors*, Wiley, New York.

Hinze J. and Tracey A. (1994) 'The contractor–subcontractor relationship: the subcontractors' view', *Journal of Construction Engineering and Management*, Vol. 120, No. 2, June 1994, pp. 274–87.

Hughes W.P. (1992) *An Analysis of Traditional General Contracting*, Construction Papers No. 12, Chartered Institute of Building, London.

Klein R. (1994) 'Tendering anarchy in UK', *Building*, 15 July, p. 30.

Massey W.B. (1992) *Subcontractors during the tender period – an estimator's view*, Construction Papers No. 2, Chartered Institute of Building, London.

Nicholls P. (1993) 'The challenge which faces the new industry review', *Contract Journal*, 5 August 1993.

Price J. (1994) *Subcontracting Under the JCT Standard Forms of Building Contract*, Macmillan, Basingstoke.

Runeson G. (1988) 'An analysis of the accuracy of estimating and the distribution of tenders', *Construction Management and Economics*, Vol. 6, pp. 357–70.

Seeley I.H. (1989) *Advanced Building Measurement*, 2nd edn, Macmillan, Basingstoke.

Uher T. and Runeson G. (1984) 'Pre-tender and post-tender negotiation in Australia, *Construction Management and Economics*, Vol. 2, pp. 185–92.

Uher T. and Runeson G. (1985) 'Subcontractor–general contractor relationship in the Australian building industry, *International Project Management*, February 1985.

8 Pricing Preliminaries

8.1 WHAT ARE PRELIMINARIES?

The preliminaries section of the tender documentation fulfils a number of functions from the estimator's point of view. At an overall level the preliminaries section provides a high-level overview of the project, including a description of the project and the site and details of the conditions of contract to be used, but the preliminaries will also include a considerable amount of more detailed information about specific issues. Information covered in the preliminaries section can therefore be divided into the following subgroups:

1. General project details

2. Contractual matters

3. Specific requirements of the employer

4. Contractor's general cost items

5. Information about works to be executed by persons other then the main contractor or which may be subject to later instructions

Each of these is considered in more detail below. While the examples used are taken from the *Standard Method of Measurement of Building Works*: Seventh Edition (SMM7), they are indicative of the kind of information that would typically be given regardless of the method of measurement actually used. It can readily be seen that, although the preliminaries section typically contains a very large amount of written information, only some of the items are actually priceable. Solomon (1993), for example, contends that an analysis of preliminaries costs shows that 80% of the total cost is accounted for by only four items (staffing, mechanical plant, access/scaffolding and site accommodation), while the addition of power supplies and cleaning raises the proportion to 90%. He goes on to write that tender documents examined by his practice show that only 20 priced items can be identified. Table 8.1, taken from Solomon (1993), shows the average proportions of preliminaries costs

98

Table 8.1 Analysis of main preliminaries items

Preliminaries items	Average % of total preliminaries
1. Staff	26.5
2. Mechanical plant	22.3
3. Access/scaffolding	18.0
4. Site accommodation	11.8
5. Power	6.3
6. Site cleaning/clearance	4.8
7. Telephone/fax	2.1
8. Temporary roads	1.8
9. Hoardings and signs	1.7
10. Watching and lighting	1.7
11. Insurances	1.7
12. All other items	1.3
	100.0

for each of the eleven major items for a series of traditional building projects ranging in value from £250 000 to £55 m.

Pricing of the preliminaries section will usually be one of the last operations before adjudication of the tender price, and will require that decisions relating to working methods, major plant, gang strengths, subcontractors, temporary works (e.g. scaffolding, roads, hardstandings, hutting) and the proposed construction programme have all been settled. This will then indicate any need for overtime working etc. and will also allow the assessment of any fluctuation in costs in the case of a fixed price tender.

Research by Tah *et al.* (1994) appears to show that contractors will each have their own checklist of items to assist the estimator in calculating site overheads. A good typical example designed for major projects is given in CIOB (1983, pp. 96–107), while Mudd (1980) gives a simpler version designed for use on smaller projects.

8.2 FIXED AND TIME-RELATED CHARGES

An important innovation under SMM7 is that provision is required to be made for items given under the 'Employer's requirements' and 'Contractor's General Cost Items' sections to be split into 'Fixed Charges' and 'Time-Related Charges'. SMM7 Section A Clause 21 defines a fixed charge as 'work the cost of which is to be considered independent of duration', while time-related charges are defined as 'work the cost of which is to be considered as dependent on duration'. The provisions are therefore in some respects similar to but not as flexible as the civil engineering method-related charges outlined in Chapter 6. The intention is plainly to provide contractors with the oppor-tunity to show more accurately in their priced bills where part of the cost of an item is fixed and part is time-related. A good example might be a tower crane, where the transport, setting up and erection costs are fixed regardless of the time the plant remains on site, whereas the hire cost, operator's wages etc. will vary depending upon the time the plant is in use.

This method of pricing is obviously of use to both the quantity surveyor and the contractor for the preparation of interim valuation payments, and has been advocated for some time: see for example Stubbington (1980). It may also aid the contractor in substantiating claims for additional payments as a result of variations, and for reimbursement of loss and expense following the granting of an extension of time, but the SMM7 Measurement Code makes it clear that there is no compulsion on the estimator to split the price. Clause 3.2 of the Measurement Code states that 'The fixed and time-related costs given for a number of preliminaries items will enable tenderers to price the elements separately *should they so desire*'. Solomon (1993), however, writes that:

> The majority of methods of measurement now call for appropriate preliminaries items to be priced on a fixed and time related charge basis. When contractors neglect to comply with this requirement the informa-tion should be obtained and analysed before any contract is placed.

While one would have to agree with the sentiment, the contention seems difficult to substantiate given the wording of, for example, SMM7.

There is also no guidance given in SMM7 as to how the time-related charges should be shown in the bills. Typical alternative formats might be as shown in Table 8.2.

SMM7 implies that time-related charges are to be given as an item, but this would seem to be somewhat counter-productive. If the information is to be of any real use it must be related to known time-scales (per day, week, month etc). If this approach is accepted then it must also be made clear whether the cost is to be related to the contract period given in the tender document or to the projected construction period as shown on the contractor's programme.

It has, however, become common practice for some contractors to move money around in tender bills (see also Chapter 11), and it is not unusual for the prices inserted in the preliminaries bill to bear little or no relationship to the contractor's actual costs. Tah *et al.* (1994) indicate that site overheads may be included either as a percentage of measured work, in the preliminaries section, or as a combination of both, while Solomon (1993) writes that:

> This [preliminaries section] is the main area within a tender where a contractor can seek to gain a competitive advantage by adjustment of

Table 8.2 Preliminaries: example formats

Employer's Requirements		£	p
Provide a temporary office for the use of the Clerk of Works and others acting on behalf of the Employer as described in General Specification clause A/26/10	F TR		
Provide sanitary facilities for the exclusive use of the Clerk of Works and others acting on behalf of the Employer as described in General Specification clause A/26/11	F TR		

Example format 1

Employer's Requirements	£	p
Provide a temporary office for the use of the Clerk of Works and others acting on behalf of the Employer as described in General Specification clause A/26/10		
Fixed charge:		
Time-related charge:		
Provide sanitary facilities for the exclusive use of the Clerk of Works and others acting on behalf of the Employer as described in General Specification clause A/26/11		
Fixed charge:		
Time-related charge:		

Example format 2

Table 8.2 (cont.)

Employer's Requirements	Fixed £	p	Time-related £	p
Provide a temporary office for the use of the Clerk of Works and others acting on behalf of the Employer as described in General Specification clause A/26/10				
Provide sanitary facilities for the exclusive use of the Clerk of Works and others acting on behalf of the Employer as described in General Specification clause A/26/11				

Example format 3

Employer's Requirements				£ p
Provide a temporary office for the use of the Clerk of Works and others acting on behalf of the Employer as described in General Specification clause A/26/10				
Fixed charge:				
Time-related charge:		wk		
Provide sanitary facilities for the exclusive use of the Clerk of Works and others acting on behalf of the Employer as described in General Specification clause A/26/11				
Fixed charge:				
Time-related charge:		wk		

Example format 4

the tender price. The preliminaries bill provides the contractor with an opportunity to make a provision for overheads and profit within his tender. While profit should not be forbidden fruit, it is a luxury which the contractor can adjust, to provide the opportunity of winning a contract.

He goes on to show that there is a close direct relationship between the proportion of the tender cost accounted for by the preliminaries element and the state of the construction market. It can therefore be appreciated that some contractors are most reluctant to break down the prices shown in the preliminaries bill any further than is absolutely necessary. It therefore follows that the percentage of the total tender price allocated to preliminaries in the tender bills will vary widely from job to job depending upon tendering and pricing strategies adopted.

The information given in each subsection of the preliminaries is now considered in detail.

8.3   GENERAL PROJECT DETAILS

This section will contain basic project information such as the name, nature and location of the project, the names and addresses of the Employer and Consultants (i.e. Architect, Quantity Surveyor, Structural Engineer, Mechanical Engineer, Electrical Engineer etc.), and lists of the relevant drawings. Only the drawings from which the bills have been prepared are specifically required to be listed, but it would also be good practice to list any drawings that are required by SMM7 rules to be included with the tender bills, and also the contract drawings (if known).

In addition information will be given about the site and the works, typically as follows:

1. Details of site boundaries, either by description and/or by reference to site plans or map references.

2. Details of existing buildings on or adjacent to the site where their presence may have an influence on cost due to their proximity causing restricted access or limitations in the use of cranes etc. or where special care is necessary, perhaps because of their historic nature.

3. Any drainage, water, gas and other mains or power services known to exist on or over the site, or any services that exist outside the site boundary and which may be affected by site operations.

4. A description of the work, giving the estimator an initial impression of the types of work involved, including details of any unusual features or

conditions. The description may be quite short, as further information is available to the estimator in the form of drawings and the remaining contents of the bill.

Most of the information given in this section is not directly priceable, but will serve to give the estimator some guidance regarding the degree of abnormality in the works (see also Chapter 12).

8.4 CONTRACTUAL MATTERS

The following details are required by SMM7:

1. The Form of Contract to be used, together with a Schedule of clause headings of the standard conditions

2. Special conditions to be imposed by the Employer, or any amendments to standard conditions

3. The insertions to be made in the Appendix to the Conditions of Contract

4. Employer's insurance responsibility

5. Any Performance Guarantee Bonds required

6. Whether the contract is to be executed under hand or under seal.

Again, while the items are not, in the main, directly priceable, the information given is essential to the estimator/contractor in determining the degree of risk imposed by the contractual arrangements (see also Chapter 12).

8.5 EMPLOYER'S REQUIREMENTS

This section is one of those for which SMM7 requires provision to be made for the insertion of fixed and time-related charges. The section will include specific Employer's requirements relating to:

1. Conditions for tender additional to those stated on the invitation letter and/or form of tender. General conditions relating to subcontracting and supply of goods.

2. General requirements for the provision, content, use and interpretation of documents, whether by the Architect, Consultants, Contractor or Sub-contractor.

3. Requirements for the general management, supervision and administration of the Works, with particular reference to time and cost. Matters which

may be covered, if not included elsewhere in the Conditions of Contract, might include:

(a) Responsibility for coordination, supervision and administration of the works, including all subcontracts

(b) Relevant insurances

(c) Recording of climatic conditions

(d) The master programme and its monitoring

(e) Arrangements for site meetings

(f) Notification of commencement and completion of the works

(g) Notice to the Quantity Surveyor before covering up work

(h) Daywork and provision of vouchers

(i) Conditions relating to reservation of title on unfixed materials

(j) Provision of site labour and plant records

4. General requirements for the quality of materials and workmanship, arrangements for supervision and inspection, completion of the work and making good of defects. This might include items such as:

(a) Protection of unfixed materials

(b) Requirements in relation to samples

(c) Setting out the works, appearance and fit of components, critical dimensions and record drawings

(d) Proposals for the rectification of defective work or materials

(e) Cleaning the works, removal of rubbish

(f) Final finishing, including touching up paintwork, easing, adjusting and lubricating ironmongery and other moving parts, and leaving the works secure on completion

5. Requirements for safeguarding the site, the works, unfixed materials, existing buildings and their contents, adjoining property, mains services and for preventing danger and nuisance.

May also include requirements for health, safety, prevention of nuisance, security, control of pollution, and protection of existing trees, services etc.

6. Employer's requirements which specifically and directly limit the Contractor's/Subcontractor's methods of operation, their sequence and timing.

The requirements given are supplementary to limitations described or implicit elsewhere.

7. Facilities, temporary works and temporary services specifically required by the Employer during construction of the Works. Employer's requirements regarding the nature, siting, removal etc. of facilities, temporary works and services, including those required by the Contractor or Subcontractors for their own use.

8. Facilities and services required to be provided by the Contractor/Subcontractor at Completion or thereafter to help the Employer operate and maintain the finished building. An example might be provision of training for the Employer's staff in the use of the building's electrical and mechanical services installations.

While much of the information given is again not directly priceable, some items (for example item 8 above) will obviously have a direct cost.

8.6   CONTRACTOR'S GENERAL COST ITEMS

Items covered will include:

1. The contractor's site management team. The size of the contractor's site organisation will vary depending upon factors such as the size of the contract, the type and complexity of the work to be undertaken, availability of staff and the contractor's staffing policy. Many contractors will have a standard schedule used for calculating site management costs. A typical example, developed from CIOB (1983, p. 99), is shown in Table 8.3.

The number of people employed on site by the contractor in supervisory and administrative roles will also tend to vary during the course of the work to suit the needs of the construction process. In assessing the cost of site staff the estimator must therefore carefully study the requirements of the construction programme. On smaller contracts people such as contracts managers, quantity surveyors and site clerks may be employed part-time on several projects, and their cost must therefore either be spread in proportion to the time spent on each site or included with the contractor's general head office overheads.

2. Site accommodation for the use of the contractor. The cost of supplying and maintaining suitable office accommodation for the contractor and the employer's representatives will vary depending on several factors, the main ones being the number of people to be accommodated, the size of offices required, the type of temporary buildings to be used, the location of the offices on site, and the amount of space available. It might, for example,

Table 8.3 Project site team checklist

Management and staff	Nr	£	Wks	Total
Management				
Contracts manager				
Site manager				
Assistant				
Trades supervision				
General foreman				
Trades foreman				
Ganger				
Engineering				
Setting out engineer				
Assistant				
Services engineer				
Assistant				
Site engineer				
Assistant				
Programming etc.				
Planner/programmer				
Assistant				
Production engineer				
Bonus surveyor				
Assistant				
Quantity surveying				
Senior quantity surveyor				
Quantity surveyor				
Assistant				
Support staff				
Clerk/typist				
Storekeeper				
Checker				
Time keeper				
Safety officer				
Watchman/site security				
Canteen staff				
First aider				
Others				
Safety officer				
			£	

be necessary to stack offices into two-storey blocks or to position them on scaffolding above street level.

The estimator will have to make a detailed build-up of the cost of the site offices for each contract, taking into account both fixed and time-related expenditure.

Fixed costs would include capital cost and depreciation, or alternatively the hire rate, for office buildings and furniture, transport to and from the site, labour and plant costs for loading and unloading, erection and dismantling.

Time-related costs would include the cost of weekly cleaning and attendance, lighting and heating costs and any rates or taxes payable to the local authority.

A typical calculation for provision of an office for the Clerk of Works is shown in Table 8.4. Similar calculations will be required for mess rooms, sanitary facilities, drying and changing areas etc.

3. Services and facilities, including power, lighting, water, telephones, storage of materials, attendance on subcontractors.

Temporary services will require very careful consideration. The estimator will need to consider availability of public supplies (e.g. electricity and water) or whether generators, water bowsers etc. will be required. Telephone costs present a particular problem, since the cost will be made up of installation charges, rental charges for the equipment and the cost of calls. The costs associated with the first two items can generally be forecast with a fair degree of accuracy, but the actual cost of calls will be subject to considerable variation. Most contracts will include a provisional sum for the cost of calls made by the architect or his or her representative, and some means of recording these is required. General attendance on subcontractors presents particular problems, and this issue is discussed in Chapter 7.

4. Mechanical plant. Provision will often be made for the contractor to add additional items. Some items of plant are used by several trades, and as it is difficult to apportion their cost accurately to each trade, they are normally priced in the preliminaries section. Typical items would be general site cranage, compressors, hoists for goods and/or passengers, and materials handling equipment, i.e. fork lift trucks, dumpers, tractors, trailers etc.

As plant priced in this section will generally be kept on site for long periods of time, the following points should be noted:

Table 8.4 Typical calculation for site accomodation

<u>Bill item</u>

Provide accommodation for the Clerk of Works. The office to be a minimum of 15 m^2 complete with desk, three chairs, plan chest and filing cabinet and to be provided with adequate heating and electric light. Maintain and keep clean and tidy for the period of the contract.

<u>Method Statement</u>

Contract period 2 years (24 months). Portacabin from own plant hire company. Internal hire rate £50 per week. Purchase furniture new plus two 1 kW electric fires. Assume 20% resale value at end of contract. Transport cabin to/from site £150 each way including crane for loading and unloading. Allow £100 for connection and disconnection of power supply.

<u>Analysis</u>

Fixed charges			£
Transport units to/from site	2 trips × £150.00		300.00
Labourer load/unload cabin	3 h × 2 × £5		30.00
Note: cranage charges included with transport costs			
Connect/disconnect power supply			100.00
Furniture:	2 fires × £40	80.00	
	3 chairs × £40	120.00	
	1 desk	125.00	
	1 plan chest	200.00	
	1 filing cabinet	150.00	
		675.00	
Less resale value 20%		135.00	
Loss of interest on £675 for two years			
say 10%/year	say	135.00	675.00
	<u>Fixed costs</u>		1105.00

Time-related charges			£
Hire charge	104 wks × £50		5200.00
Fuel (electricity)	heating	2 kW	
	light	1 kW	
		3 kW	

Carried forward:			5200.00

Brought forward:	5200.00

Assume lights and fire in use for 50% of total contract period; therefore total consumption will be:

104 weeks × 5 days × 8 h × 3 kW/h × 50%=	
6240 units × 5 p	312.00

Clean out – labourer say 0.5 h/day
5 days/week × 104 weeks =

260 h × £4.50	1170.00
Consumables say	100.00
<u>Time-related costs</u>	6782.00

<u>Rate per month = £282.58</u>

<u>Total cost to preliminaries bill (fixed charge plus time-related charges): £7887.00</u>

(a) The weekly 'all-in' cost of the driver and any attendant labour (i.e. banksman) should be calculated, allowing for anticipated overtime working, likely bonuses, operators' and attendants' NWR plus rates, service times etc.

(b) The hire cost of the plant should be taken as a weekly rate, based on 50 hours use/week, irrespective of the actual hours worked on site.

(c) Other points the estimator should consider include transport to/from the site, unloading/loading of plant and equipment, initial erection/dismantling costs and testing charges on cranage.

The actual time period that the plant is to be on site will need to be assessed from the proposed construction programme. The cost of transporting items of plant and equipment is often included in the preliminaries even if the use of the equipment has been priced in the unit rates. It may be difficult to apportion transportation charges to the individual rates unless operational estimating techniques are used. The cost of unloading and loading the plant, together with any costs arising from the need to erect or dismantle the plant on site, will also often be taken under this heading.

5. Temporary works. Typical items will include general scaffolding, fencing, hoardings and temporary access roads.

Table 8.5 shows a typical calculation for the cost of a temporary access road.

Table 8.5 Temporary access road

Bill item

Location and access

The site is situated within the grounds of the existing primary school on part of the existing playing fields. Access will be from Main Street via a temporary access road 195 m long to be constructed by the contractor and maintained for the period of the contract. The road is to be fenced as necessary in order to prevent vehicles encroaching onto the remaining grass areas. The road is to be removed upon completion of the building works and the ground left ready for reinstatement of topsoil and seeding by the Employer after practical completion.

Method Statement

Proposed 4.50 m wide with 1.50 m high chestnut pale fencing to both sides. Road to be 200 mm thickness of compacted limestone (38 mm – dust) laid on a Fibretex mat. Strip topsoil 150 mm deep and stockpile. No reduced level dig. Remove road and reinstate topsoil and seed on completion. Allow labourer 4 h/week and 5 tns stone for filling in potholes during the contract period. Salvage value of fencing 50% of new cost. Contract period 40 weeks. Allow £100 for forming opening in fence and reinstate.

The excavator will be required on site for the foundation works and the cost of initial transport will be included elsewhere, but the machine will go 'off hire' upon completion of the initial foundation works.

Analysis

Total area of road $= 195.00 \times 4.50 = 877.5$ m^2 say 878 m^2
Fencing (both sides) $= 2 \times 195.00 = 390$ m
Volume of topsoil to remove $= 878.00 \times 0.15 = 131.7$ m^3 net
Volume of hardcore required $= 878.00 \times 0.20 = 175.60$ m^3 net

Fixed charges		£
Initial road constructionForm opening in boundary fence and later reinstate	lump sum	100.00
Site strip (based on 10 m^3)		
International IOOB (NB transport included elsewhere)		
(including driver costs £15.00 per hour)		
Machine excavates 10 m^3/hour $= £1.50$/m		
Total net volume removed $=131.70$ m$^3 \times £1.50 =$		197.55
Carried forward		£297.55

Continued   £

                                                    Brought forward   297.55

Disposal with 3 m^3 dumpers to site spoil heap. Machine
excavates 10 m^3/h
Bulking factor say 25%. Total net volume removed =
12.50 m^3 bulked spoil for disposal. Dumper capacity
3 m^3 therefore say 4 loads/hour to move

Cycle time is as follows: load   0.25
                          travel (avg 200 m say) 0.20
                          unload   0.10
Cycle time/time per load   0.55 h
Cycle time/load = 0.65/0.55 = say 2 dumpers required
Total excavation 131.70 m^3 machine works at 10 m^3/h =
          13.70 h say 2 days.
Dumper cost = daily hire charge   £40.00
              driver £6.00 all in × 8 =   £48.00
                                          £88.00 per day × 2 = 176.00

'Fibretex' blanket
Total length required 195 m × 4.50 m wide. Rolls are 4.50 m wide
× 100 m long so say 2 rolls including waste × £105.00 per roll =   210.00
Lay Fibretex mat. Labourer at 10 m/hour 195 m = 19.50 h × £5.60 109.20

Hardcore bed
Materials. Total volume (compacted) 175.60 m =
175.60 × 2.20 tns/m^3 = 386.32 tns + waste say 5% =
405.64 tns × £6.50 =   2636.66
Plant. Machine lays 15 m^3/h therefore 175.60 m^3 will take
12 h × £15   180.00

Level and compact hardcore
Roller with 2 man gang
              driver £6.00 all in × 8 =   £48.00
              mate £5.50 all in × 8 =   £44.00
              daily roller hire   £25.00
                                                £117.00

Total area 878 m^2 × 40 m^2/h = 21.95 h. Use 2 rollers
for 12 h each = 3 days × £117.00/day =   351.00

Carried forward   3960.41

<u>Continued</u>   £

                                          Brought forward   3960.41

Removal

Machine not on site so transport required for 2 trips × £35.00 =   70.00

Excavate hardcore. Total volume of hardcore = 175.60 m^3

Machine works at 8 m^3/hour and is required for say 22 h × £15 =   330.00

Remove hardcore from site. Use 6 m tipper.

Excavation rate = 8 m^3/h + bulking say 30% therefore 10.40 m^3/h

to cart away. Loading time for 6 m^3 = 6/10.4 = 0.58 h

Cycle time =	load	0.58
	travel to tip	
	20 km × 45 km/h	0.44
	unload	<u>0.10</u>
		<u>1.12</u> h

Nr of lorries = cycle time/hours to load = 1.12/0.58 = 1.93.

Say 2 lorries required. Total excavation time

22 h × 2 lorries × £12.50 =   550.00

Tipping charge £5 per load. Nr of loads =

175.60 m^3 + 30% = 228.28 m^3

228.28 m^3 ÷ 6 m^3/load = 38 loads × £5 =   190.00

Fencing. Posts at 3 m centres. Basis of analysis 75 m.

Labour	fix fence	3.00 h		
	fix posts			
	25 nr × 0.5 h	12.50 h		
	dismantle			
	75 m/20 m per h	<u>3.75</u> h		
		<u>19.25</u> h × £5.50 =	£105.88	

Materials	fence posts 25 nr × £1.50	£37.50	
	fencing 75 m × £2.50	<u>£187.50</u>	
		£225.00	

Less 50% salvage value of fencing

50% × £187.50 =	<u>£93.75</u>	£131.25
Total for 75 m =		<u>£237.13</u>

Rate per metre = £3.16 × 195 m × 2 =   <u>1232.40</u>

              <u>Total fixed charge</u>   <u>£6332.81</u>

Continued

Time-related charges	£

Maintenance
Include 1 labourer for 4 h/week + 5 tonnes stone
Contract period 40 weeks. Total labour requirement =

40 weeks × 4 h per week = 160 h × £5.00 =	800.00
Limestone. 5 tonnes × £6.50 =	32.50
Total time-related charges	832.50

Total to Preliminaries Bill = 6332.81 + 832.50 = <u>£7165.31</u>

8.7   WORKS BY PERSONS OTHER THAN THE MAIN CONTRACTOR OR SUBJECT TO INSTRUCTION

This section will include details of:

1. Any works carried out or materials to be supplied by the Employer.

2. Any work to be executed by nominated subcontractors together with any attendances required

3. Any materials to be supplied by nominated suppliers

4. Any work to be carried out by Statutory Undertakers

5. Sums to be included in the respect of works to be carried out on dayworks

6. Any provisional sums

This section therefore consists largely of specified sums of money which the estimator is required to include in the tender. The most important items requiring pricing by the estimator will be those dealing with special attendance required on nominated subcontractors, and these items will require very careful consideration (see also Chapter 7). Examples of special attendance might include hoisting heavy equipment into position, providing special scaffolding for suspended ceilings and provision of special lighting and power. The pricing of such items requires great care, and despite the requirements of the various standard methods of measurement, often only the sketchiest of details are given in the tender bills.

8.8 REFERENCES

CIOB (1983) *Code of Estimating Practice*, 5th edn, Chartered Institute of Building, London.

Mudd D.R. (1980) 'Pricing preliminaries', in *The Practice of Estimating*, pp. 14–20, Chartered Institute of Building, London.

Solomon G. (1993) 'The market place effect', *Chartered Quantity Surveyor*, October 1993, pp. 9–11, Royal Institution of Chartered Surveyors, London.

Stubbington D.T. (1980) 'Preliminaries: improving cash flow', in *The Practice of Estimating*, pp. 21–8, Chartered Institute of Building, London.

Tah J.H.M., Thorpe A. and McCaffer R. (1994) 'A survey of indirect cost estimating in practice', *Construction Management and Economics*, Vol. 12, pp. 31–6.

9 Plan and Specification Projects

9.1 INTRODUCTION

Previous chapters have dealt primarily with the pricing of work let on the basis of bills of quantities provided by the client, but a considerable number of projects are let without bills, and in this case the contractor is required to calculate the price solely on the basis of drawings and a specification.

This chapter is concerned with the pricing of work let in this way, and highlights some of the principal additional problems which face the estimator when quantities are not provided as part of the tender documentation.

There is no mandatory rule as to what types of project should be let on a plan and specification basis, and what types of project call for bills of quantities. The choice is left to those responsible for preparing the tender documentation, and there is no doubt that in some cases inappropriate decisions are made. In each case, however, the decision ought to reflect consideration of the following issues:

1. Projects for which bills of quantities are prepared will generally take longer and cost more in professional fees in the pre-contract stages.

2. The general level of tender prices for projects let on the basis of plans and specification is likely to be higher than for similar projects let using bills of quantities to reflect the increased risk taken by tendering contractors.

3. Bills of quantities provide a good information base from which to assess the value of work completed for interim payments, and for the valuation of variations and additional work.

4. The discipline of producing bills of quantities may result in projects which are more completely designed than projects let on the basis of plans and specifications.

The decision as to whether to use plans and specifications or bills of quantities ought to be taken after careful consideration of:

1. Project value

2. Any pre-contract time constraints

3. Project complexity

4. The likelihood of variations

Hence projects of comparatively low value but with a high degree of complexity and perhaps a high probability of variations (for example alteration and refurbishment schemes costing only a few hundred thousand pounds) may be better let using bills of quantities, whereas much more costly but less complex projects (for example the construction of a simple warehouse building, or even the refurbishment of a large number of similar local authority dwellings involving upgraded kitchens and bathrooms and costing in total perhaps several million pounds) might be quite acceptably let on the basis of plans and specifications.

9.2   TENDER DOCUMENTATION

Where quantities are provided as part of the tender documentation some standard set of rules, a 'Standard Method of Measurement', will have been used at least to measure the quantities, and in some cases, for example civil engineering works, will even dictate the format of the bills of quantities. Both the amount of work to be included in the tender and its precise specification are therefore given to the tendering contractors, and this information then provides a firm and uniform basis upon which all tenderers can calculate their prices. In addition, most standard forms of contract provide for any errors of measurement found in the bills, or for discrepancies between the bills and the project drawings, to be corrected and for the contract sum to be adjusted accordingly. Any risk, therefore, from the tenderer's point of view, is confined to calculation of the price and not to the calculation of the quantities.

In the case of projects let on the basis of 'plan and specification', however, no such rules apply. Although the code of procedure for Coordinated Production Information undoubtedly could (some would argue should) be followed in the preparation of the tender documents, in practice there is a wide variation in the type and quality of information provided to tendering contractors. At the lowest end of the scale the client may not even appoint a professional advisor, but may go directly to the builder, providing little in the way of information except perhaps a few rough sketches and notes, relying on the builder to fill in the missing information. In this case the process effectively becomes a design and build arrangement. At the other end of the scale, however, assuming that the client's professional advisors have done their job properly, full sets of drawings and a detailed specification will be provided. The spectrum between these two extremes is obviously very wide, but the more detailed the information provided by the client/design team the less the theoretical degree of risk taken by the contractor in preparing a tender, and the easier it should be, in theory at least, to compare the various tenders submitted.

In practice, however, if they were to be honest, some opportunistic contractors would argue that from their point of view the less comprehensive the project documentation is the greater the opportunities to increase the price at final account stage through variations and claims. This is obviously not in the best interests of the client, and professional advisors should perhaps point this out to those clients who are anxious to save either money or time during the pre-contract stage by skimping on the pre-contract documentation.

9.3   TYPES OF SPECIFICATION

Ayres (1984) defines a specification as:

> a description of an article or method so complete that it can be bought or built by others to the complete satisfaction of all concerned

Although in the UK the Coordinated Project Information Initiative coupled with the National Building Specification (NBS) and the National Engineering Specification (NES) has established a formal 'good practice' framework for the production of project specifications (see for example CPI (1987, p. 20) and BPIC (1987)), there is no mandatory format. Specifications may therefore range in scope and completeness from, at one extreme, a few simple notes on the project drawings, to comprehensive, often bulky, documents which resemble bills of quantities without the quantities.

An example extract from the simplest and perhaps most traditional form of specification is shown in Table 9.1. As can be seen, the specification is simply a list of descriptions governing the standards of materials and workmanship to be used in the project, with no cash column and therefore no provision for the contractor to indicate prices for individual items of work.

The major disadvantage, from the point of view of the client and its professional advisors, of specifications prepared in this way is the lack of any kind of breakdown of the tender sum, thus making it very difficult to assess the value of work completed for interim valuation payments. For this reason specifications are sometimes provided with a cash column, as shown in Table 9.2.

Table 9.1 Typical traditional specification without cash column

	CARPENTRY	
100	Workmanship	The quality of all workmanship shall comply with BS1186 Part 2
101	Timber for carpentry	The softwood for carpentry shall, unless otherwise specified, comply with BS Code of Practice 112 Table 1 Group 2 and shall be free from decay and insect attack with a moisture content not exceeding 22% of the dry weight at the time of erection and with visible characteristics of dimensions not exceeding those given in Table 4 of this Code of Practice. All carpentry timber shall be of the full scantling specified.
102	Flat roofs	Frame and fix the flat roofs as shown on the drawings using 50 × 75 or 50 × 100 joists as appropriate set at 400 mm centres. Include for notching ends of joists to steelwork and cutting and pinning to existing walls as necessary. Provide and fix softwood firring pieces to the top of each joist to obtain the required falls shown on the drawings. Provide and fix 50 × 25 triangular tilt fillets at all boundaries and abutments where necessary or where shown on the drawings.

In addition to providing a cash column, tenderers are sometimes asked to complete a schedule of the unit rates used in calculating the tender price, which may then be used as a basis for the valuation of variations. A typical example is shown in Table 9.3. Note, however, that there is no method of verifying that the rates inserted in the schedule are those that the contractor has actually used in the preparation of the estimate, and there may in reality be no link at all between the schedule of rates and the tender price.

9.4   RISK

Senior (1990) points out that:

> The contractor bases his estimate on the accuracy and sufficiency of the information provided by the drawings and the specification/schedule of works.

Table 9.2 Specification with cash column

	Alterations	£	p
	<u>Main Office</u> (Floor area 18.36 m, ceiling height 2700 mm)		
a	Remove pair of fully glazed doors 55 mm thick complete with frame and two opening lights and plywood panel over, overall size 1840 × 3110 mm. Remove door curtain and track, 140 mm wide timber lining to opening and 90 × 35 mm moulded architrave to internal reveals.		
b	Build up lower part of opening in 250 mm thick brickwork hollow wall with two skins of 100 mm thick insulating concrete blockwork to form new window opening 1840 mm wide × 2170 mm high. Provide and build in purpose-made timber window to match that existing in the adjacent office and glaze with 4 mm clear sheet glass. Make good plaster reveals internally up to the new frame, point around the exterior of the new window with mastic as described elsewhere, and finish the exterior blockwork with coloured 'Tyrolean' render to match the existing adjacent panels. (Decoration work all described elsewhere).		

It has already been shown that it is likely that the documentation for projects let using plans and specifications will not be as complete as that where bills of quantities are provided, and it therefore ought by now to be clear that contractors tendering on this basis take a rather greater share of the risk. The primary risk, in addition to risks posed by the completeness or otherwise of the tender documentation, arises because the tenderer is responsible for the measurement of the work, and must take the responsibility for any resulting errors or omissions.

In addition, clauses such as the following are not unknown:

Any items of work not shown on the drawings and/or not described in the specification but which nevertheless are required in order that the works shown on the drawings and/or described in the specification may be carried out will be deemed to be included in the tender submitted.

While the legal validity of clauses such as this may be somewhat dubious, they are indicative of the common desire to place as much of the risk as possible with tendering contractors.

Table 9.3 Example extract from Schedule of Rates

BOROUGH OF ANYTOWN
MODERNISATIONS, WELFARE AVENUE
SCHEDULE OF RATES

The Contractor is to fill in the following schedule with the rates on which his tender is based in accordance with the Conditions of Contract in order that variations, comprising extra work to or work omitted from the contract may be valued in accordance with the said Conditions.

Description of Work	Unit	Rate
Excavation for surface trenches including earthwork support, compacting bottoms, backfill and removal of surplus spoil	m^3	
Hardcore filling placed in 150 mm thick layers including compaction and blinding	m^3	
Concrete (Quality B) in foundations including all necessary formwork	m^3	
250 mm thick cavity wall in engineering bricks as described in foundations including forming cavity, galvanised cavity ties and concrete cavity filling	m^2	

9.5 BUILDER'S QUANTITIES

Where quantities are not provided with the tender documentation it is obvious that the contractor must prepare the necessary quantity information in order that a price for the work may be calculated. The amount of measurement required and the degree of detail required will vary from project to project, depending largely upon the size and complexity of the scheme, and responsibility for this work may rest with the estimator, with the firm's quantity surveyor, or with an outside consultant quantity surveyor appointed for the purpose. There are many different approaches to the production of quantities of this type, and there are no mandatory 'standards' of the kind set out in the various Standard Methods of Measurement. Pasquire (1993) does, however, attempt to derive both a standard set of measurement rules and a formal methodology for the process, based on extensive research of the methods used in the mid to late 1980s in a number of contracting organisations.

Quantities of this type may sometimes be termed 'approximate quantities', but this is a misnomer. While the various items of work will not be measured to the same degree of detail as one would expect to find in a bill prepared under a Standard Method of Measurement, it will defeat the whole object of the exercise if the actual quantities are not measured with reasonable accuracy. A better generic term, and that used by Pasquire in the title to her paper, is 'Builder's Quantities'.

The style and the degree of detail incorporated in the builder's quantities for any particular project is likely to be constrained by the following factors:

1. Project size and project complexity.

2. The time usually allowed for submission of tenders for plan and specification projects is often short, and there may therefore be insufficient time for detailed measurement.

3. The costs of producing builder's quantities, not only for successful tenders but for unsuccessful ones as well, must be covered by the allowance included by the contractor in respect of overhead charges on successful tenders.

There are therefore very powerful incentives to persuade the contractor that the amount of measurement carried out on each job should be the minimum necessary to allow a price to be prepared. Pasquire (1993, p. 16) identified the following factors, among others, as being important in the derivation of her measurement rules:

1. Each building type should be documented separately.

2. The building design, site conditions and proposed method of working must govern the method of measurement adopted.

3. The measurement unit depends upon the buying unit or the method of procurement for the resources measured.

4. Measured items should identify all the resources required, in particular the labour requirement, and not just be based on the final quantity of finished work required.

Two possible approaches are illustrated in the following examples.

9.5.1   Example 1: Garden Wall

Figure 9.1 shows the partial demolition and re-construction of a domestic garden wall. The section to the boundary with the village hall requires merely repointing, but the remainder, the whole length of the front boundary, requires completely rebuilding. The existing wall is constructed from grey

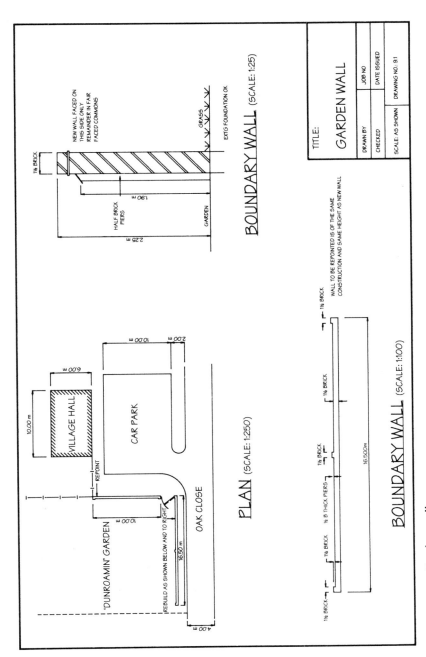

Figure 9.1 Garden wall

Table 9.4 Estimate example 1

Estimate for boundary wall – 'Dunroamin'

Assumption: water and toilet facilities available on site   £

Demolition

Volume of existing wall

	16.50	
	0.33	
	2.25	12.25
3/	0.33	
	0.11	
	1.90	0.21
		12.46 m^3

Allow 100% for bulking say 25 m^3 would require 6 skips. Not practical so use 6 m^3 lorry. 4 trips should be OK for 1 day. Use JCB to load.

Lorry hire including driver	1 day	80.00
JCB hire	1 day	95.00
Labour say 2 men	16 h × £5.73 (1994 all-in rate)	91.68

Note: No tipping charges.

New Wall

Commons:
main wall 16.50 × 2.10 = 34.65 m^2 × 177 bks/m^2 =   6133
piers 1.90 ÷ 0.075 × 1.5 × 3 = say   114
                                                                6247

Facings:
main wall 16.50 × 2.10 = 34.65 m^2 × 74 bks/m^2 =   2564
ends 2 × 0.33 × 2.10 = 1.39 m^2 × 74 bks/m^2 =   103
                                                            2667
Coping: 16.50m ÷ 0.075 × 2 =   440
(including waste)

Materials

		£
Commons: 6247 − 2667 =	3580 @ £98 per 1000	350.84
Waste 5%		17.54
Facings:	2667 @ £152.25 per 1000	406.05
Waste 7.5%		30.45
Blues: Waste included	440 @ £199.50 per 1000	87.78
Carried forward		1159.34

Brought forward £1159.34

Mortar (say 1:3 mix)

Cement	62.00/tonne delivered
Unload 0.5 h/tn × 3.38	1.69
	63.69

Materials for mortar

0.50 tonnes cement × £63.69/tonne =	31.85
1.67 tonnes sand × £9/tonne =	15.03
	£46.88

Note: mixer included later.

Assume frogged bricks therefore 0.60 m^3 of mortar
required per 1000 bricks.
Total no of bricks 6247 + 440 = 6687 × 0.60/1000 =

4.01 m^3 × £46.88 =	187.99
Waste 5% =	9.40

Tile creasings – plain tiles 265 × 165

Therefore say 4 nr per 165 mm of wall = 16.50 ÷ 0.165 × 4 = 400
Add say 6 nr for each pier therefore

total required = 418 × £134/1000 =	56.01
Waste 5% =	2.80
Mortar for creasing 2/16.50 × 0.33 × 0.01 =	
say 0.11 m^3 × £46.88 =	5.16

Labour

Total nr of bricks is 6687. Most of the work is in straight runs so say
45 bricks/hour/man. Use 2 + 1 gang

6687 ÷ 45 × 2 =	74.30 h

Add for pointing

2 × 16.50 × 2.25 =	74.25
3 × 2 × 1.90 × 0.12 =	1.37
2.25 × 0.33 =	1.49
16.50 × 0.33 =	5.45
	82.56 m^2

82.56×0.10 h/m^2/man =	4.13 h
Prepare top of wall and set creasing say	4.00
	82.43 h

Carried forward	1420.70

		Brought forward	1420.70

Gang rate: 2 bricklayers × £6.76 =   13.52
               1 labourer × £5.73 =   5.73
                                             £19.25

Total labour requirement 83 h @ £19.25 =   1597.75

Repoint existing wall

Materials

Mortar say 30% of allowance for a new work HB thick per side

2 × 10.00 × 2.25 =	45.00
2 × 0.33 × 2.25 =	1.49
2 × 3 × 1.90 × 0.12 =	1.37
10.00 × 0.33 =	3.30

$51.16 \text{ m}^2 \times 0.02 \times 0.3 =$
                                    $0.31 \text{ m}^3 \times £46.88$ 14.53

Waste say 10%   1.50

Labour

Rake out and repoint say 0.75 h/m^2 for 2 men
    51.16 m^2 × 0.75 = 38.37 h × £12.49 =   479.24

Plant

Total bricklaying gang time
        Build wall   83 h
        Repoint   38 h
                               121 h @ 8 h/day = say 16 days.
5/3.5 mixer @ £30 per week for 16 days × £30 ÷ 5 =   96.00
Fuel – say 5 h/day × 2 litres per h = 160 litres × £0.25   40.00
Oil 16 days × £0.50 per day =   8.00

Scaffold

Take one lift for full length of new wall. Hire for 2 weeks to include for repointing.

Tube

3 × 16.50	49.50
17 × 2.00	34.00
9 × 1.20	10.80
	94.30

        say 95 m × 2 weeks = 190 m/weeks × £0.05 =   9.50

Carried forward   3667.22

	Brought forward	3667.22
Fittings say 100 × £0.10 × 2 weeks =		20.00
Boards say 5 boards + toe bd		
6 × 16.50 = say 100 m × 2 weeks × £0.15 =		30.00
Additional labour to erect and move scaffold		
say 2 labourer days 16 h × £5.73 =		91.68

Clear up site

Labourer 1 day 8 h × £5.73 =		45.84
Skip say 1 day × £25.00 =		25.00
		3879.74
Add for overheads and profit 25%		969.04
	Total estimate £	4849.68

wirecut facing bricks In English Garden Wall bond with a Staffordshire Blue brick coping set on a two-course plain tile creasing.

In cases such as this it would be common for the work to be considered simply on a time and materials basis, similar to the operational estimating methods described in Chapter 6. A typical calculation for the estimate might be as Table 9.4.

9.5.2   Example 2: Foundation to Press Shop Extension

Figures 9.2 and 9.3 show the foundations to an extension to an industrial factory unit. This project is rather larger than Example 1, and in this case a typical 'builder's quantities' measurement approach has been used. An example set of unpriced builder's quantities is shown in Table 9.5. Note particularly that while the measurement is accurate (so the quantities are in no sense approximate) the items measured are much less detailed than would be the case in a bill prepared using, for example, SMM7, and also that a number of items that might normally be measured separately are typically combined when using this approach.

The measurement time is thus considerably reduced, and although some of the time saved will be offset by the time taken to build up the more complex unit rates required, the method should show considerable overall time savings when compared with the preparation of a fully measured and priced bill of quantities. Calculation of the unit rates themselves is not considered here, but is straightforward, as explained in Chapter 4.

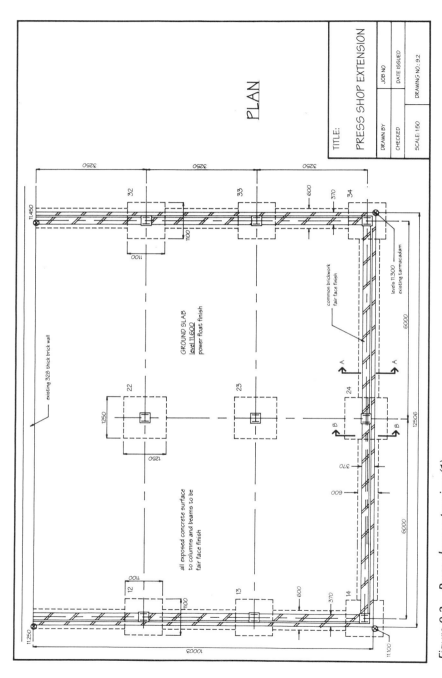

Figure 9.2   Press shop extension (1)

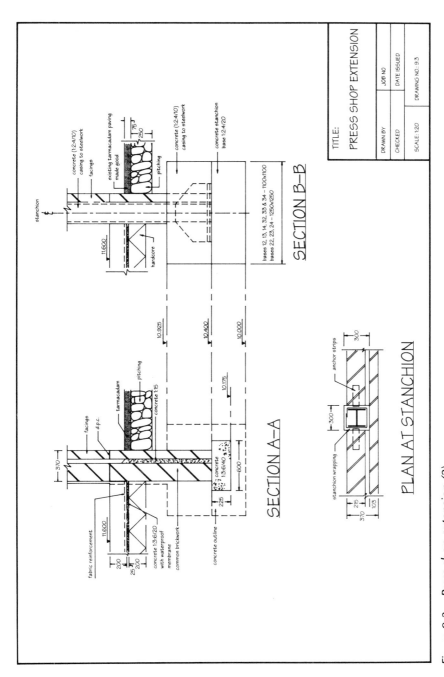

Figure 9.3   Press shop extension (2)

Table 9.5 Estimate example 2

Dims			Description	Quant	UM	Rate	£
			Estimate for press shop foundation (drgs nrs 9.2 and 9.3)				
	10.10		*Excavation and disposal (reduce levels, trenches, pits including break up pavings)*	59	m^3		
	12.70						
	0.25	32.07					
	31.77						
	0.60						
	0.95	18.11	2/10.003				
			20.006				
			12.506				
			32.512				
6/	1.10		2/0.37 0.740				
	1.10		31.772				
	1.13	8.20					
3/	1.25		11.600				
	1.25		0.150				
	1.13	5.30	11.450				
		63.68	10.175				
			1.275				
			less 0.325				
			0.950				
			11.450				
			10.000				
			1.450				
			less 0.325				
			1.125				
			Ddt. Last				
6/	1.10						
	0.60						
	0.95	3.76	*(no earthwork*				
	1.25		*(support reqd.*				
	0.60						
	0.95	0.71					
		59.21					
			Page 1			£	

Dims			Description	Quant	UM	Rate	£
	31.77		*Concrete in foundations*	8	m^3		
	0.60						
	<u>0.23</u>	4.38	100.40				
			<u>100.00</u>				
<u>6/</u>	1.10		<u>0.40</u>				
	1.10						
	<u>0.40</u>	2.90					
3/	1.20						
	1.20						
	<u>0.40</u>	<u>1.73</u>					
		9.01					
6/	1.10		*Ddt last*				
	0.60						
	<u>0.23</u>	0.91					
	1.25						
	0.60						
	<u>0.23</u>	<u>0.17</u>					
		<u>7.93</u>					
	10.10		*Compact bottom of*	1.28	m^2		
	<u>12.70</u>	<u>128.27</u>	*escavation*				
	23.92		*Hardcore backfill*	6	m^3		
	0.23						
	<u>0.72</u>	3.96	31.77				
6/	1.10		6/<u>1.10</u> 6.60				
	0.73		<u>1.25</u> <u>7.85</u>				
	<u>0.20</u>	0.96	<u>23.92</u>				
	1.20						
	0.83		0.95 1.13				
	<u>0.20</u>	0.20	<u>0.23</u> <u>0.93</u>				
2/	1.20		<u>0.72</u> <u>0.20</u>				
	1.20						
	<u>0.20</u>	<u>0.58</u>	1.20 0.60 1.10				
		<u>5.70</u>	<u>0.37</u> <u>0.37</u> <u>0.37</u>				
			<u>0.83</u> <u>0.23</u> <u>0.73</u>				
			Page 2			£	

Dims			Description	Quant	UM	Rate	£
	31.77		Cavity brickwork in	34	m²		
	1.20	38.12	common bricks; one brick				
			outer skin; half brick inner				
			skin; cavity, fill and ties				
			11.600 10.925				
			10.400 10.400				
			1.200 0.525				
6/	1.10		Ddt last				
	0.53	3.50					
	1.20						
	0.53	0.64					
		33.98					
2/	1.29	2.40	Tie new brickwork to	2	m		
			existing				
			11.600				
			10.925				
			0.675				
	2		Concrete in column casing				
			300 × 300 × 675 mm				
			including formwork,				
			anchor strips and				
			reinforcement	9	nr		
			(bwk not deducted)				
6/	1.10		Concrete in casing to				
	1.10		stanchion base plate	6	m³		
	0.53	3.85					
3/	1.20		100.925				
	1.20		100.400				
	0.53	2.29	0.525				
		6.14					
	31.77		Dpc to cavity wall; one				
			brick and half brick skins	32	m		
			Page 3			£	

Dims			Description	Quant	UM	Rate	£
12.14			*Floor slab; 200 mm*				
9.63	116.91		*concrete with A142 fabric*				
			reinforcement, damp proof				
			membrane and 200 mm				
			thick blinded hardcore bed.	117	m^2		
			10.003 12.506				
			0.370 0.370				
			9.633 12.136				
32.91			*Make good tarmac paving*				
			up to new wall	32	*m*		
			31.772				
			2/0.37 0.740				
			32.514				
			avg. 2/0.20 0.400				
			32.912				
32.31			*Extra over cavity wall for*				
0.23	7.43		*facings and pointing*	7	m^2		
			32.512				
			less 2/0.103 0.206				
			32.306				
						£	
			Collection				£
			Page 1				
			2				
			3				
			4				
						£	
			Add for overheads and			£	
			profit				
			Total estimate			£	
			Page 4			£	

9.6 REFERENCES

Ayres C. (1984) *Specifications for Architecture, Engineering and Construction*, 2nd edn, McGraw-Hill, New York.

BPIC (1987) *Project Specification, a Code of Procedure for Building Works*, Building Project Information Committee, UK.

CPI (1987) *Co-Ordinated Project Information for Building Works, A Guide with Examples*, Coordinating Committee for Project Information, UK.

Pasquire C. (1993) *Builders' Quantities for contractors' management*, Occasional paper No. 55, Chartered Institute of Building, London.

Senior G. (1990) *Risk and Uncertainty in Lump Sum Contracts*, Technical Information Service Paper No. 113, Chartered Institute of Building, London.

10 Overheads, Profit and Project Financing

10.1 INTRODUCTION

In order to be able to formulate a tender bid, a contractor needs to include a number of other factors in addition to the costs of the direct inputs to the project. Specifically it needs to know about its indirect costs; the costs of operating the business and providing the necessary finance to remain solvent, and also about the costs of any supplementary finance required for the particular project.

These factors are each considered separately.

10.2 INDIRECT COSTS

Indirect costs may be defined as those costs that the contractor faces whether or not it actually carries out any work. In crude terms the commercial value for construction work will include the total of the direct costs, that is the net estimate, with appropriate additions for indirect costs represented basically by overheads and profit. On top of this the bid price may then include an adjustment to reflect the perceived risk and the degree of utility the contractor places on getting the job, here termed the risk margin. The bid price will therefore be built up as shown in Figure 10.1.

Each component must be considered separately, and one needs to be especially careful not to confuse overheads, profit, additional project financing costs and risk margin. Companies must obviously plan their financial activity for the year, and the annual plan will therefore include a prediction of the cost of overheads and an assessment of the base level of profit required to present a reasonable return to the company's shareholders. Note that the baseline profit figure will include provision for the cost of the normal finance needed to keep the company afloat, but some projects may require additional financing to be arranged. Overheads, calculation of the base profit margin and some elementary aspects of supplementary project financing are considered here, the issue of risk margin is considered in more detail in Chapter 13.

Net estimate
+
Overheads
+
Additional project financing costs
+
Required profit
+
Risk margin (may be negative)
↓
Bid price

Figure 10.1   Bid price.

10.3   OVERHEADS

Overheads represent the fixed costs of running the company regardless of whether the company does any work or not. Costs will therefore include factors such as head office staff salaries and on-costs, the cost of providing and maintaining company cars, head office rental or mortgage payments, and operating expenses, such as telephones, heating and lighting. In a competitive market there is an obvious relationship between the level of overheads that a company can support, the amount of economic activity in the company (often measured by the company's turnover), and the level of profit that can be achieved, and this relationship will form the basis of the company's business plan.

The plan will therefore include an anticipated overheads component based upon the projected level of activity planned for the year. Most companies will project their anticipated overhead expenditure for the coming year based upon past costs, with allowances for any additional resources required and for inflation.

10.4   FINANCIAL PLANNING AND BASELINE PROFIT

Baseline profit is defined here as the amount of money the contractor must make in order to be able to service its forthcoming projected financial commitments, and this therefore requires an assessment of the basic finance which the company will require during the year.

Although construction companies are generally characterised by a low investment in fixed assets, and the industry is generally of a 'payment on account' character, construction companies often suffer from liquidity problems for a variety of reasons. Some of the more common include retentions, drops in output caused by bad weather, under-valuation of work in progress, extended contract periods and late settlement of contractual claims. In addition, the contractor will usually be paid in arrears for work completed. On most projects valuations of work completed will be prepared each month and forwarded to the client for payment. Contractors therefore need to be able to fund the work in progress until the payment is received. The time lag between work being completed and receipt of the payment varies greatly depending upon the form of contract and the habits of the client, but under most forms of contract it is likely that the contractor will have to wait for at least three weeks after the valuation of the work before receiving payment. The industry therefore suffers badly from liquidity problems, and all contractors need funds to finance their overheads, stocks of materials and work in progress, and to obtain a high enough level of liquidity to be able to meet bills when they fall due.

The nature of the work done will affect the amount of funding required. Speculative development may require much more money 'up front' than contracting unless the contractor is able to pre-sell units before they are built – not an uncommon occurrence in some parts of the world when property prices are seen to be rising and buyers indulge in property speculation.

Available sources of finance may be divided into long- and medium-term finance, usually used to start or expand the business, and short-term finance, which may be required to overcome short-term cash flow problems. Providing adequate finance to maintain liquidity becomes a greater problem as companies become larger and more complex in structure, and construction markets contract. Financial planning is therefore necessary to ensure the full and most advantageous use of available resources, in order that the company can meet its commitments, and so that the company's cash flow situation remains satisfactory. Financial planning may be divided up into long- and short-range planning.

Long-range planning (up to 5 years) involves the overall consideration of probable markets, trends in demand, inflation, changes in company structure, new materials, new techniques etc., and their effect upon the capital requirements and likely cash flow demands. Sources of long-term finance will include retained profits from previous years, bank loans, shares of various kinds, merchant banks and debentures including mortgages, floating charges and loans. Short-range financial planning (into the foreseeable future) usually means the preparation of cash flow forecasts of increasing accuracy as the projects tendered for and obtained become a reality. Sources of short-term finance include overdrafts, loans from clearing banks or finance houses, private loans, the use of company provisions set aside for payment of tax or VAT and credit extended by suppliers and subcontractors. Since construction is considered financially to be a high-risk business, institutional funders will require carefully thought through business plans.

In order to prepare a business plan the contractor must therefore consider:

1. The proposed level of activity for the year, usually denoted by projected turnover

2. The finance necessary to support the proposed level of activity

3. The return that needs to be earned on turnover in order to service the debt.

As an example, assume a construction company plans a turnover of £10 000 000 for the coming year. The contractor must then make a prediction about the level of investment required to provide a satisfactory level of liquidity. If we then assume that required investment is roughly 10% of anticipated turnover, then £1 000 000 of investment is required, upon which the contractor must return say 15%.

The calculation of baseline profit is therefore as follows:

Required profit = 15% of £1 000 000 = £150 000

Profit on turnover is therefore £150 000 ÷ £10 000 000×100 = 1.5%

Assume that overheads, based on last year's costs with additions for inflation etc. are £500 000; then the required recovery of overheads, as a percentage of turnover, is:

£500 000 / £10 000 000 × 100 = 5%

The combined baseline percentage on turnover required to cover the overheads and finance the necessary debt is thus 6.5%.

Financial planning also means monitoring the company's performance and cash flow and taking remedial action as the year progresses, and the baseline percentage required may therefore change as time goes by. As an example, consider what would happen if the anticipated turnover were not achieved. Assume that turnover only reaches £8 500 000. Basic required earnings are still as before, i.e. £650 000 for profit and overheads, and to earn this level of return on a reduced turnover of £8 500 000 will therefore require a mark-up of 7.65%. It has already been shown (Chapter 1) that contractors making tender bid decisions must know not only what their 'static' cost components are but must also have an accurate idea of the overall performance of the company against the business plan and a reasonable knowledge of their costs per unit of production (see also Hillebrandt (1985)).

10.5   PROJECT FINANCE

In addition to the normal finance required to maintain the business in a healthy state, it is likely that from time to time the contractor may have to arrange additional finance to cope with the demands of a specific project, and the costs of this additional finance must be included in the tender bid. In order to decide what finance is required for each project, the contractor must prepare a cash flow analysis for the work before finally submitting the tender bid. This factor has recently assumed increasing importance with the growth in the use of non-traditional methods of procurement. There is increasing pressure for contractors to provide clients with a one-stop service, including project financing, so much so that some (e.g. Tiong and Yeo, 1993) see the provision of project finance as a useful marketing tool.

It is therefore necessary to consider both the preparation of project cash flow forecasts and the possible sources of project finance that might be available.

10.6   CASH FLOW FORECASTING

In simple terms, cash flow forecasting involves charting the flow of money into and out of the company over a known period of time. During the periods when the flow of cash into the company is greater than the cash flowing out the cash flow is said to be positive and the company is (usually) making a profit; conversely, when the amount of cash flowing out of the company is greater then the cash coming in then the cash flow is said to be negative, and the company must draw on its financial reserves in order to remain solvent. The company therefore obviously hopes to make sufficient money when the cash flow is positive to cope with the negative flow demands, and over some time period, usually the financial year, to have generated sufficient positive cash flow for the business to show a profit.

Preparation of a cash flow forecast therefore requires that the prices for items of work in the priced bill of quantities be related to the contractor's programme, and it is here that operational estimating methods really come into their own. Accuracy of the cash flow forecast is therefore heavily dependent upon the accuracy of the programme and the priced bill.

Work package costs, which may not necessarily be the same as the values entered in the priced bill (see Chapter 11) are divided into labour, plant, materials, and domestic and nominated subcontract costs, and are listed on a weekly payments schedule as shown in Table 10.1. Note that the objective is to show cash flow out of the company, and figures will be entered according to when payments need to be made, not when the work will actually be done. As a guide, the following shows when payments for the various types of expenditure are likely to have to be made:

Wages	weekly
Materials and hired plant	4–6 weeks after delivery
Domestic subcontractors	4–6 weeks after work done

Table 10.1 - Example payments chart (part only)

Factory for Jones & Son   Payments chart

Operation		Month 3	Month 4	Month 5	Month 6	Month 7	Month 8
Subs. bwk.	L	6000.00					
	M		9000.00				
	P		600.00				
	SC						
Hardcore slab	L		3000.00				
	M			4500.00			
	P			560.00			
	SC						
Concrete slab	L				4000.00		
	M					5550.00	
	P					1200.00	
	SC						
Steel frame	L	150.00					
	M						
	P		550.00				
	SC			55000.00	40000.00		
Supers. bwk.	L		6000.00	6000.00	1500.00		
	M			9000.00	9000.00	1000.00	
	P						
	SC						
Cladding	L			150.00	150.00		
	M						
	P						
	SC					20000.00	15000.00
External drains	L		2500.00				
	M			5000.00			
	P			1250.00			
	SC						
Totals		6150.00	21650.00	81460	54650.00	27750.00	15000.00

Nominated subcontractors   17 days after issue of the architect's
                              certificate

The expenditure for each contract is then aggregated onto a master schedule to show total expenditure for all projects.

A similar process is then followed for income, using projected values for work planned to be completed in each period taken from the priced bill, as shown in Table 10.2. Note that again the objective is to show when the payments will be received, not when the work is done, and the figures will therefore have to be adjusted to take account of retentions and the fact that payment will not be

Table 10.2 Example receipts chart (part only)

Factory for Jones & Son		Anticipated receipts				
Retention %	5%					
Operation	Month 3	Month 4	Month 5	Month 6	Month 7	Month 8
Subs. bwk.		21000.00				
Hardcore slab			11000.00			
Concrete slab					12500.00	
Steel frame			57000.00	40000.00		
Supers. bwk.			16000.00	16000.00	3000.00	
Cladding					20500.00	16500.00
External drains			9500.00			
	0.00	21000.00	93500.00	56000.00	36000.00	16500.00
Less retention	0.00	1050.00	4675.00	2800.00	1800.00	825.00
Totals	0.00	19950.00	88825.00	53200.00	34200.00	15675.00
Less expenditure	6150.00	21650.00	81460.00	54650.00	27750.00	15000.00
Net cash flow	−6150.00	−1700.00	7365.00	−1450.00	6450.00	675.00

received until perhaps three weeks after preparation of the valuation. Incoming cash flows are again summed and entered onto a master schedule to show the total projected income to the company during each period.

Once the two schedules have been prepared they can either be shown graphically or on a cash flow chart, and this can then be used to assess short-term finance needs. The use of a simple computer spreadsheet can greatly ease the preparation of cash flow forecasts.

10.7   SOURCES OF PROJECT FINANCE

There may, however, be certain periods of heavy negative cash flow, perhaps the start of a new project, where the financial reserves are inadequate but it is anticipated that a strong positive cash flow will follow and that in the long run the venture will be profitable. It is at these times that the company will need to seek short-term finance in order to overcome the temporary funding problem.

The two major sources of project finance available to a construction contractor are either internal finance or finance obtained from one of the financial institutions, which would include the merchant banks.

10.7.1   Internal Finance

It is possible for a contractor to extend its capital base by increasing its share capital. This option can be attractive, since the return on shares is geared to the performance of the company, but is more likely to be used as a source of business expansion capital rather than short-term finance. Other options, which may be open in some cases, are private loans from shareholders, or the use of company reserves set aside for future tax payments.

10.7.2   Financial Institutions

Financial institutions are banks, insurance companies and pension funds. Banks will traditionally look closely at the assets of a company rather than the projects in hand in order to ensure sufficient security for the loan. Options will include overdraft facilities or period loans.

10.7.3   Merchant Banks

Merchant banks do not, in general, lend their own funds. Instead, they concentrate on raising money through the financial markets to meet specific needs. Merchant banking can therefore be defined as the structuring of a transaction, for a fee, between those who have the available finance and those who need it. This type of finance is therefore only normally used for large schemes. Merchant banks can also be useful internationally, particularly for projects in developing countries where the financial markets may be unwilling to take the risks. In this case merchant banks may be able to advise on the arrangement of finance through the national export credit agencies of the developed world, which are established by Governments largely to assist their own exporters to obtain overseas contracts. The terms of export credit finance tend to be competitive compared with commercial rates, but the finance is only available in specific areas of the world.

10.8   TYPES OF PROJECT FINANCE

There are now many types of project finance, and the following can only give a brief overview of some of the more common. Many substantial financial transactions become very complex and involve a combination of different types of finance.

10.8.1   Bridging Finance

Bridging finance consists generally of a short-term interest-bearing loan for a period of anything up to three years. This type of finance tends to be expensive.

10.8.2   Mortgages

There are many different types of mortgage available. Contractors could therefore obtain funds by raising a mortgage against fixed assets, for example a head office building or even a partially completed speculative development.

In recent years mortgage finance has become increasingly sophisticated, with a wide variety of repayment patterns.

10.8.3   Non-Recourse Loans

Non-recourse financing has become popular with the growth of build/operate/transfer type projects, where the contractor, often in joint venture with a number of partners, designs, constructs and operates a facility under some form of licensing agreement for a specified period of time. At the end of the concession period the completed project is handed to the client, usually a public authority, at no charge. Such projects therefore always begin with a very large debt, and the necessary income to repay the loan and charges, the construction cost and the developer's profit is generated out of revenue during the period of the concession. This type of project has become popular with the current fashion around the world for privatised infrastructure provision, for example toll roads, toll bridges and tunnels. This form of finance restricts the lending institution to recovering any unpaid debt from the project rather than from the borrower: in other words, the lender has no recourse to the contractor's assets, thus limiting the contractor's risk. Lenders will pay close attention to the project debt/equity ratio; in other words, the more of its own money the contractor is prepared to put into the venture the keener lenders will be to participate.

10.9   REFERENCES

Hillebrandt P. (1985) *Economic Theory and the Construction Industry*, 2nd edn, Macmillan, London.

Tiong R. and Yeo K.T. (1993) 'Project financing as a competitive strategy in winning overseas jobs', *International Journal of Project Management*, Vol. 11, No. 2, pp. 79–86.

11 Adjudication and Bid Submission

11.1 INTRODUCTION

It has already been shown that the process of compiling a tender for construction work is conventionally divided into two separate stages: first, calculation of the anticipated cost to the contractor of completing the work, and second, the setting of a price which the contractor will then quote to the client, usually in competition with others. The process of converting the contractor's estimate into a tender bid is called *adjudication*. Adjudication is a management activity which, particularly in a competitive tendering situation, usually involves the exercise of subtle and subjective commercial judgement in arriving at the bid figure.

In crude terms it could be said that the adjudication process, in so far as it applies to competitive tendering, involves making an assessment of the highest price the contractor can quote and still get the work, but it is really more than this. Of course, the price must be both high enough to cover the contractor's costs together with an acceptable level of profit, and yet be pitched at a level which will persuade the client to accept the offer in preference to any of the others, but the decision is not simply about submitting the lowest price and covering costs.

If it is accepted that the contractor really should be trying to maximise its profits, it will ideally seek to pitch its price at a level which will give it the best possible return while still being acceptable to the client. Tassie (1980) expresses it very succinctly:

> Tender adjudication is concerned with getting the job at the best price; securing it in competition by the smallest possible margin; and on the best commercial terms procurable...

Consider, for example, the following tender list:

Contractor A: £2 010 000

Contractor B: £2 105 000

Contractor C: £2 105 500

Contractor D: £2 150 010

Contractor E: £2 200 000

Contractor A has obviously submitted the best price and, all other things being equal, will get the job. However, A's price is almost £100 000 below the next lowest tender. The contractor could have quoted a price of, say, £2 100 000, and still have been the one most likely to have been awarded the project. It has given away a possible £90 000 in additional profit which could have been earned had its adjudication been better.

Considerable research has been carried out into the ways by which contractors can improve their chances of submitting the 'best' bid. Different approaches have included the attempted development of various mathematical models of the bidding process, methods based on historical data, statistical bidding models, and models based on econometric techniques. There appears to be considerable anecdotal evidence that despite the theoretical research most managers make adjudication decisions intuitively rather than on the basis of factual information. Bidding strategies, bidding models, and the factors which contractors take into account in formulating their tender bid are all discussed in detail in Chapter 13, and this chapter therefore concentrates mainly on the mechanics of the adjudication process, the management information systems required to support it, and factors to be considered in the submission of the bid and, if successful, the priced bill of quantities.

The adjudication process may itself be divided into two parts. The first part of the process involves deciding what price the firm would ideally like to charge to complete the work (in other words the true commercial value), whereas the second part of the process involves deciding on the tender bid. It is in this second part of the process that commercial judgement is exercised in order to attempt to submit the winning bid. Davies (1980) explains:

The overall aim of the considerations and calculations leading to the tender is to arrive at the figure which the firm requires in return for carrying out the construction works. It is not to arrive at a figure which it is thought will be lower than one's competitors. There will, however, always be occasions when the decision will be taken to submit a figure higher, or lower, than the straightforward commercial value. Nevertheless it is important to arrive at the latter figure first and then make an adjustment for any management venture element.

11.2   THE ESTIMATOR'S REPORT

The major part of the information required for the adjudication meeting will be supplied by the estimator. The estimate documentation for a large construction project is, however, likely to be very bulky and will almost certainly contain a large amount of irrelevant detail, and in order that management can make informed decisions about the tender bid, it is obviously essential that it should have a summary of the key information contained in the estimate. This key summary is called the estimator's report, and its purposes are:

1. To bring together all of the pertinent facts which have influenced the estimator during the preparation of the estimate

2. To highlight for management the various matters which are considered to be cost significant

3. To identify any special or unusual contract conditions or risks

The report, like any other good report, should be concise but comprehensive, and will normally attempt to highlight the unusual features of the project rather than repeating large amounts of standard information. In the case of contract conditions, for example, the manager making adjudication decisions will be familiar with the various Standard Forms of Contract, and there would therefore be little point in repeating all of the standard contract wording. What the decision-maker really wants to know is what is different or unusual about this particular project that might affect the tender price levels.

While the format of the report may vary from company to company, it is suggested that the report should contain the following information:

1. A brief description of the project and the suggested method of construction, together with a note of any identified technical or contractual problems.

2. A note of any special risks.

3. An executive summary of the main features of the conditions of contract, concentrating in particular on any variations to standard forms or any unusual or onerous obligations or contract conditions.

4. An assessment of the quality and completeness of the design information.

5. A note of any major assumptions made in the estimate.

6. The estimator's assessment of the probable profitability of the project.

7. Any pertinent commercial information which the estimator has gathered, for example information about market conditions, other tenderers etc.

8. A note of any special terms or conditions quoted by subcontractors.

9. The time for which the tender is required to be open for acceptance.

10. The need for any qualifications required to the tender.

11. Details of the client, architect, quantity surveyor and other consultants.

12. Any special conditions imposed by the employer (e.g. bond, special insurances).

13. An analysis of the estimate to show the total amounts included in respect of:

(a) own net labour costs

(b) materials costs

(c) plant hire charges

(d) domestic subcontractors' work

(e) work covered by PC Sums

(f) provisional sums

In order to ensure that things are not forgotten, it is a good idea to use a standard format for all estimators' reports within the company. Individual contractors may prefer to develop their own pro forma for this purpose, but a good general purpose example is given by the CIOB (1983, pp. 118–25).

The actual decision on the bid price will usually be taken by a small group of senior managers or, in a small company, perhaps by the owner or chief executive acting alone. Nonetheless, it is important that the decision-maker has all of the necessary information, and that all of those involved in compiling the estimate have the opportunity to contribute any specialist knowledge which they may have acquired in the process. CIOB (1983) points out that in larger organisations this may well involve either two separate meetings or at least a meeting in two parts, the first part including all of the interested parties to examine and review the estimate, and the second comprising only the senior decision-maker(s) to settle the bid price.

11.3   BID SUBMISSION AND PRESENTATION

Working from the estimator's report, those charged with the adjudication task will then make their assessment of the bid price, after which the Form of Tender can be completed and submitted. Harrison (1993), however, points out that, far from being the end of the bid submission stage, this may only be the start of the process:

It is becoming increasingly common in some types of work for the tender submission to be only the first stage in a series of meetings, discussions and negotiations where both the client and the contractor are seeking to obtain the best result. The client is looking for possibly lower prices, higher quality or faster completion and the contractor is looking to increase profitability possibly by offering alternative methods and tenders.

It is also common, especially perhaps for large projects or those let under non-traditional procurement arrangements, for example management contracting or variants of the design and build model, for contractors to be required to present their bid proposals formally to a meeting of the client and its professional advisors. Young (1993) goes further when she writes that:

> The team presentation to a prospective client has become increasingly important. Important in so far as the client expects to meet the construction team who will carry out the project and who can demonstrate that they are able to do the job. It follows that members of the team must develop presentational competencies which are beneficial in winning work.

This assertion is verified by the author's conversations with clients, project managers and contractors in the course of a recent research project investigating procurement methodologies for large hospital buildings. On one large (£32 m) design and build project the project managers stated that, despite initially ranking the various submissions against a detailed set of criteria, none of the schemes proved to be a clear winner until the various consortia involved were each asked to present their schemes in person, when a clear winner rapidly emerged. Fellows and Langford (1993), in their study of marketing in the construction industry, conclude that:

> Clients are... placing more attention on the contractor's performance record, past relationships, financial stability and the expertise of its personnel. All contractor's personnel must be part-time marketeers....

There can be little doubt that, no matter how good the contractor and its staff, the ability to present that expertise in the most effective way must be a vitally important skill. Young (1993) gives detailed consideration to the factors that need to be considered in the preparation and delivery of high-quality presentations.

11.4   SUBMISSION OF THE PRICED BILL

Pricing of the bill of quantities to be submitted in support of the tender poses a number of problems for the contractor. At the very simplest level it is likely that the estimator will have priced the bill net, and that the total of the net priced bill will need to be reconciled with the tender figure; in other words, the mark-up decided by management during the adjudication stage will need to be incorporated into the bill rates. This may be done in a variety of ways. For example, the mark-up can be allocated as a straight percentage addition across all of the measured work, or, alternatively, the value of the mark-up could be incorporated into the preliminaries element. Both methods have advantages, and sometimes contractors may choose to use a combination of both methods. If the profit element is included in the preliminaries section contractors might feel that their profit is to some extent 'protected' in the event of variations leading to significant reductions in the measured value of the work. On the other hand, since the rates in the priced bill will be used as the benchmark for the valuation of variations, if variations lead to a substantial increase in the scope of the work it is distinctly possible that the contractor could be out of pocket.

In effect, the real situation is likely to be much more complex than this. Available evidence (e.g. Green, 1989) would appear to indicate that 'tactical pricing' of bills of quantities, sometimes called 'unbalanced bidding', is now evident in a significant proportion of cases. Tactical pricing is taken here to mean manipulation of the prices inserted in the priced bill by artificially inflating some rates and deflating others in order to gain some financial advantage. While tactical pricing may be frowned upon by the client's professional advisors, the benefits of the process to the contractor can be considerable and the use of a variety of different techniques is advocated by a number of authors (see for example Park and Chapin (1992) and Stark and Mayer (1983)). Neither is the use of such devices restricted to Western capitalism. Tong and Lu (1992), for example, working in the Tsinghua University in Beijing, have developed a complex mathematical rate loading model designed 'to objectively exploit variation trends in client provided quantities'.

Green (1989) identifies three basic methods, namely front end loading, individual rate loading (or 'item spotting') and back end loading, but to these should be added the special class of techniques designed to unbalance rates across a whole tender in order to maximise the present value of the contract as a whole.

11.5   FRONT END LOADING

It has already been shown that the combination of the 'payment on account in arrears' method with the retention arrangements commonly used in construction projects is likely to mean that contractors need to provide significant finance to support the project, particularly in the early stages. Some contractors may therefore attempt to partially overcome this problem by pricing the early trades high, thus hopefully ensuring a strongly positive cash flow in the early stages of the project. While this may help at the beginning, however, it does mean that the contractor must make compensating reductions to its rates elsewhere in order for the tender sum to remain the same. Since the priced bill is often used as the contractor's budget in the post-contract cost control phase, unbalanced pricing during the tender stage can pose considerable problems for the contractor's project manager and project quantity surveyor during the construction stage unless the original pricing strategy is carefully documented. Experience would seem to show that this is rarely done.

11.6 'ITEM SPOTTING'

'Item spotting' or individual rate loading is normally applied to take advantage either of perceived errors in the bills of quantities or to maximise the contractor's return on remeasured work. Even where firm bills of quantities are provided, prudent contractors will always carry out some kind of check measurement on the quantities of major bill items in the course of preparing an estimate, and it is by no means uncommon for this process to reveal errors in the billed quantities. Since, under most standard forms of contract, errors in the bills of quantities are adjustable in the same way as varied work, it is easy for contractors to take advantage of such errors during the estimating process, artificially inflating the price for under-measured items and deflating the price for items found to be over-measured.

The main area in which contractors can attempt to maximise their opportunities in this way is through the use of projects let on the basis of bills of approximate quantities and subject to remeasurement. Most civil engineering works fall into this category. Again it is common in tenders of this type for estimators to carry out check measurement in order to gauge the potential reliability of the quantities given in the bills. Tong and Lu (1992) describe the development of a mathematical model designed to allow contractors to optimise the rates quoted once the discrepancies have been identified.

11.7 BACK END LOADING

Green (1989) makes the point that the prevailing inflation rate clearly has an effect on the merits of front end loading for fluctuations contracts, since although it aids the contractor's initial cash flow situation it may well have a detrimental effect on the amount received in fluctuations payments at the end of the project, and this may be especially important where some form of formula fluctuations system is used. The view receives some support from McCaffer and Baldwin (1984, pp. 245–6), where they write that:

The application of the civil engineering price adjustment formula to contracts changed the approach of contractors who had previously concentrated on reducing their capital lock-up by attempting to gain payment for all works at the earliest possible opportunity. If the rate of inflation was higher than the cost of capital, then by improving their contract cash flow contractors were depriving their companies of adequate compensation as calculated by the Baxter formula for increased costs...

Given the above it is at least feasible that contractors could devise a strategy to optimise prices so as to take maximum advantage of expected fluctuations in the cost of certain parcels of work as calculated by the formula rules. This would almost certainly involve loading the rates of items to be completed late in the project.

11.8   MAXIMISING THE NET PRESENT WORTH OF THE CASH FLOW

Stark and Mayer (1983) use linear programming techniques to develop a process for optimising prices across a whole project by maximising the present worth of the payments based on item quantities and durations. Green (1989) reports that, in the course of an experiment to test the validity of such approaches:

A systematic approach to optimising the net present value of a tender was recently applied to a live project in central Scotland [the result of which was that] the net present value of the tender was increased by 0.3% of the contract sum.... While 0.3% may not appear to be significant, when compared to the reported prevailing mark-ups of 1–2% then such a percentage addition surely cannot be dismissed.

11.9   CONCLUSIONS

While there is considerable evidence of the practice of rate loading of one kind or another in priced bills of quantities, it would seem that front loading and item spotting are by far the most common. It also appears that, in general and at present, the techniques used in practice are subjective and opportunistic: there is little evidence that sophisticated mathematical techniques such as linear programming are in common use, perhaps partly because the techniques are not well understood by working estimators.

Consultant quantity surveyors will attempt to prevent contractors from submitting bills priced in this way because of the possible consequences if things go wrong. In the case of front loading, for example, in the early stages of construction the work will effectively be over-valued in interim certificates.

This then means that if the contract were to be terminated for some reason, for example because of insolvency by the contractor, then the client would be likely to have to pay considerably more than the remaining value of the original contract in order to have the work completed by someone else. Quantity surveyors, in checking priced bills, will therefore attempt to identify unbalanced bids and will seek to have the imbalance removed. While this sounds highly laudable, quantity surveyors' room for manoeuvre in this respect is somewhat limited, since one of their principal frames of reference for determining whether a rate is reasonable or not is the rates inserted in previous tender bills, and one would in any case expect a fairly wide coefficient of variation. Beeston (1975), for example, quotes likely coefficients of variation ranging from 45% for excavation work to 13% for glazing. McCaffer and Baldwin (1984, p. 11) see this issue very clearly:

> The value of these data for these purposes is suspect and can be undermined by the adjustments made by contractors in entering rates against bill items. One such adjustment is 'rate loading'.... Such rate loading may be shown up by comparison, but if all tenderers indulge in similar tactics to broadly the same degree such devices cannot be identified by comparison.

In practice, therefore, it is highly unlikely that, except in the most blatant of cases, quantity surveyors will be able to say with any degree of certainty that rate loading has taken place. Even if there is a strong suspicion that the priced bill is severely unbalanced, if the contractor refuses to amend its rates there is in truth little constructive that the quantity surveyor can do other than advise the client of the possible consequences of accepting the tender.

11.10   SUMMARY

This chapter has considered some of the general background to the adjudication process. Tendering is both a science and a gamble, and it can be argued that management should attempt to increase the science and reduce the gamble. While it will never be possible to remove the speculative element – the uncertainty – altogether, the following, paraphrased from Davies (1980), provide a good set of guidelines to support the manager's commercial judgement:

> 1. Ensure that the estimating team is consistent. Consistency and reliability are the key characteristics needed in estimators. When considering a potential tender figure the first essential is to have confidence in the estimated cost and be reassured that it has been prepared on a basis consistent with the estimates looked at yesterday, last week and last month,

and that this basis produces as accurate a forecast as can reasonably be expected in the face of the many uncertainties.

2. Work as closely as possible within the framework of the firm's tendering policy and turnover and profit targets. Make use of all suitable financial control tools. Develop a mistrust of setting aside facts, figures and solid experience in favour of playing hunches.

3. Cultivate resilience; if the last six tenders submitted were not successful, do not panic and make hasty unsound decisions. Provided the estimator's figures are reliable, no amount of wishful thinking is going to boost production levels. Do not waste time guessing what the competition is going to do; take account of the competition by all means, but do it on the basis of fact.

4. When times are hard, do not be frightened to cut back. Overheads must be kept in check at a level which the ongoing workload can support.

11.11 REFERENCES

Beeston D.T. (1975) 'One statistician's view of estimating', *Chartered Surveyor Building and Quantity Surveying Quarterly*, Vol. 12, No. 4.

CIOB (1983) *Code of Estimating Practice*, Chartered Institute of Building, London.

Davies F.A.W. (1980) 'Preparation and settlement of competitive lump sum tenders for building works', in *The Practice of Estimating*, Chartered Institute of Building, London.

Fellows R. and Langford D. (1993) *Marketing and the Construction Client*, Chartered Institute of Building, London.

Green S.D. (1989) 'Tendering: optimization and rationality', *Construction Management and Economics*, Vol. 7, pp. 53–63.

Harrison R.S. (1993) *The transfer of information between estimating and the other functions in a contractor's organisation – or the case for going round in circles*, Construction Papers No. 19, Chartered Institute of Building, London.

McCaffer R. and Baldwin A.N. (1984) *Estimating and Tendering for Civil Engineering Works*, Granada Technical Books, London.

Park W.R. and Chapin W.B. (1992) *Construction Bidding*, John Wiley, New York.

Stark R.M. and Mayer R.H. (1983) *Quantitative Construction Management*, John Wiley, New York.

Tassie C.R. (1980) 'Aspects of tendering: converting a net estimate into a tender' *The Practice of Estimating*, Chartered Institute of Building, London.

Tong Y. and Lu Y. (1992) 'Unbalanced bidding on contracts with variation trends in client-provided quantities', *Construction management and Economics* Vol. 10, pp. 69–80.

Young B.A. (1993) *A professional approach to tender presentations in the construction industry*, Construction Papers No. 17, Chartered Institute of Building, London.

12 Risk and Uncertainty in Estimating and Tendering

12.1 INTRODUCTION

This chapter begins the examination of risk and uncertainty in the preparation of estimates and tenders for construction projects. There are two major problems involved:

1. Will the contractor's tender be low enough to be accepted by the client?

2. If accepted, will the eventual financial position of the project on completion be acceptably close to the forecasts made in the tender?

Following an initial examination of the nature of risk and uncertainty, and a very superficial review of some aspects of risk analysis, this chapter examines the nature of the risks and uncertainties posed by the project and by the professional team and the risks and uncertainties normally considered in the estimating process. Consideration of the problems posed by the bidding market is deferred until Chapter 13.

12.2 THE NATURE OF THE CONSTRUCTION BUSINESS

All construction projects are, by their very nature, economically risky undertakings, and contracts let on the basis of competitive tenders tend, for the contractor, to be the riskiest of all. The problem, like so many others in construction, is not new. A quantity surveyor writing almost a century ago in 1900 wrote that (Blake, 1900):

Responsibilities are sometimes thrown on the builder when estimating, by leaving to his discretion some matter of doubtful yet ascertainable value; a matter which a little investigation on the part of those arranging the contract would free from any doubt or uncertainty whatever, and thus enable the competing builders to price it at fair value instead of

154

allowing a good margin to cover such contingency. Every point on which there is any doubt, and every matter as to which there may be the slightest misunderstanding during the execution of the contract should, in justice to all parties, be thoroughly threshed out before the contract is signed. Another occasional source of injustice... is the impracticality of plans and specifications.

Some indication of how little progress has been made in the last 100 years may be gleaned from the fact that many construction contracts are still put out for tender on the basis of incomplete information. Another quantity surveyor, writing in 1990, says (Senior, 1990):

Over many years the building industry has been aware of the difficulties relating to the placing and management of contracts. In an attempt to overcome these difficulties modifications to the established procedures have been introduced from time to time since the Banwell report identified where limitations existed.... These initiatives have failed.

It appears that even the introduction of Coordinated Project Information has not solved the problem (Burridge, 1994), although Burridge claims that in this case it is not so much the system which is at fault as the fact that the system is not being properly used.

It must, of course, be recognised that all projects, no matter how well planned or documented, will still contain some element of risk (e.g. the weather, strikes by workers or material suppliers), but it would appear that, in many cases, the clients and consultants making up the demand side of the industry seem to have decided that eliminating the uncertainties in the tendering process causes more problems than it solves, particularly since clients are seeking shorter and shorter procurement periods. This being the case, the tendency has been to develop more and more complex Conditions of Contract to try to control the consequences of the uncertainties inherent in the construction process. The issue of risk posed by the chosen procurement methodology will be considered in detail later.

It is during the processes of estimating and tendering that the contractor has to evaluate all of these risks and uncertainties, since the offer submitted at this stage, if accepted, will form the mainstay of the contractual relationship formed between the parties, and will to a large extent dictate the contractor's eventual profit on the job.

In addition to the risks implied by the nature of the project, and to those specifically dealt with by the Conditions of Contract, it is evident that even though the processes of estimating and tendering may be based on scientific principles they are themselves subject to considerable areas of uncertainty and risk. The process of estimating is, by definition, to do with making a forecast of the likely costs of the inputs to the construction process, and since it is only a forecast of the contractor's expenditure, it must be accepted that the estimate itself must be subject to some uncertainty. The tendering process is even more uncertain. Under normal circumstances the contractor has no way of knowing for certain at the time of tender whether the bid it submits will be both low enough to be acceptable to the client and also high enough to enable the contractor to make an acceptable profit.

An understanding of the risks and uncertainties inherent in the tendering and estimating processes is therefore important for two main reasons:

1. To help the contractor to decide on the level of mark-up which will give it the best possible chance of winning the project at an acceptable price.

2. To try to ensure, in the case of successful tenders, that the project makes the projected contribution to profits once the job is completed.

Research by Tah *et al.* (1994) appears to show that contractors deal with risk (termed 'quantifiable risk') and uncertainty (termed 'unquantifiable risk') in different ways:

All contractors classified risks into two categories: quantifiable risks and unquantifiable risks. When the risks are quantifiable the estimator includes the appropriate costings for the risks in the cost estimate.... Where the risk is unquantifiable the amount added is based on management's perception of the situation.

12.3   RISK AND UNCERTAINTY

An important first step is to define the meaning of the terms 'risk' and 'uncertainty'. Risk, defined by Rowe (1977, p. 463) as 'the potential for realisation of unwanted, negative consequences of an event', arises when the assessment of the probability of a certain event is statistically possible. Risk is insurable. Uncertainty, defined by Rowe (1977, p. 466) as 'the absence of information; that which is unknown', arises when the probability of the occurrence or non-occurrence of an event is indeterminate. Uncertainty is not insurable (Hillebrandt, 1974, p. 163). Risk is mathematically assessable, given the availability of sufficient data, whereas uncertainty is not. Hillebrandt also points out that there is no hard and fast division between risk and uncertainty, and the occurrence of some events can be moved from the category of uncertainty (i.e. they are considered to be indeterminate) to that of risk by the collection of better information. Weather statistics are a good example.

The information which needs to be made available in order to remove some event from the realms of uncertainty and therefore allow the risk to be assessed can therefore be divided into three basic types:

1. Information that cannot, at present, be known or discovered.

2. Information that is not presently known but which could, given the necessary research or data collection mechanism, be obtained.

3. Information that, although known by someone, is either not available to the decision-maker or for which the decision-maker does not have the skills to understand.

Data which could be obtained by research might include, for example, the costs to the firm of preparing estimates for various types of project. This is an area of uncertainty until the research has been carried out. Once the research has been carried out, the cost of preparing tenders becomes more certain and the likely cost of preparing a tender for a new scheme moves into the area of risk. The more comprehensive the data the more accurately the cost can be estimated and the more the risk can be reduced. Consider also the risk that the contractor might not be paid on time. In the case of a contractor who has worked many times for the same client it is likely that the contractor will be able to make a reasonable assessment of the risk that it will not be paid on time for future projects. On the other hand, a contractor working for a new client for the first time will have no first-hand data on which to base such an assessment. In the absence of any external data (credit ratings etc.) the possibility of not being paid on time is thus much more uncertain.

In either of the above cases the data are knowable and could be discovered by research. Furthermore, it is likely that the contractor will have the necessary skills to understand and use them. In contrast, consider the question of whether the contractor's tender for a project will be less than its competitors. In the absence of any data documenting the contractor's previous success or failure rates against the other contractors bidding for this specific project this is plainly an area of uncertainty, but even if the contractor has collected some data on past tender submissions, it may still not possess the necessary skills to enable it to use and interpret the data; indeed it may not even realise that such information could be useful to it at all. Fine (1987), in calling for an improved set of estimating models, asserts that uncertainty is inevitable in construction projects and that it must be planned for accordingly:

Uncertainty is not ignorance or inadequacy. It is an essential content of our projects. Small amounts of uncertainty do not always cause severe problems, large amounts do. But we do not yet have a measure that enables us to say where the boundaries between small and large uncertainties lie, though it is clear that small uncertainties in large projects seem to behave like large uncertainties in small projects.

It is therefore obviously vitally important in the understanding of risk and uncertainty to identify, in any particular situation, whether the required information is discoverable, and if so at what cost, and whether, having discovered it, the potential user has the necessary skills to use it effectively. If the answer to any of these points is 'no', then some subjective assessment of the effects of the residual uncertainty must be incorporated into the tendering and estimating process.

12.4   RISK EVALUATION

Once the risks have been identified some mechanism is required to quantify and evaluate them. Some very sophisticated risk analysis and management techniques are available and are apparently widely used in other industries. Williams (1994), for example, discusses their use in the defence industry, while Bowers (1994) discusses some issues derived from experience in the aircraft industry. There is, however, some evidence to suggest that the techniques commonly used in construction are somewhat cruder. Tah *et al.* (1994) report that their UK survey, although admittedly based on a small sample, showed that none of the respondents used any form of statistical analysis to determine risk, and Kangari (1991), while discussing American construction experience, writes that:

> Most managers rely primarily on their judgements, rules of thumb, and expertise.... The conventional algorithmic models developed in the past few years for risk analysis are not generally accepted by management for decision making under uncertainty.

Several techniques might be useful, but perhaps the simplest and most common is to attempt to assess the effects of the particular event occurring in terms of time and cost in the context of probability of occurrence of each of the risk events. These could then be summed to give an overall cost assessment. In mathematical terms:

$$RP = p_1R_1 + p_2R_2 + p_3R_3 + \dots + p_nR_n$$

where RP is the risk premium, $p_1, p_2, \dots, p_n$ are the probabilities of occurrence of each risk ($0 < p_n < 1$), and $R_1, R_2, \dots, R_n$ are the costs involved for each identified risk.

The assessed total cost could then be expressed as a percentage of the net cost.

This model is very simplistic, since it assumes that each of the risk events is independent of each other, and it has already been shown that in many areas this is not the case. The model could also be improved fairly easily simply by expressing the probability of occurrence of each event in terms of a probability distribution and using a computer to carry out a Monte Carlo simulation.

Many more sophisticated risk modelling techniques have been developed. Berny and Townsend (1993), for example, present a methodology using a software package called VISIER for analysing risks taking account of time and dependence with the risk event modelled as one of a number of types of probability distribution. Ren (1994) presents the concept of the risk life cycle, including not only the predicted financial consequences and the probability of occurrence, but also time properties (i.e. the time period within which the risk could occur) and the influence of relationships between different risks. Possible risk relationships are shown in Table 12.1. Ren goes on to report on a case study using the PREDICT software package which incorporates these characteristics.

Table 12.1 Risk relationships

Independent
A particular risk event is not affected by any other risks in the system

Dependent
A particular risk event (B) is dependent upon the occurrence of another risk event (A). If A does not occur then B will definitely not occur, but if A does occur B may occur.

$A \rightarrow B$

(A) may have more than one risk dependent upon it, i.e. (A) may give rise to one or more events (B_1), (B_2),...,(B_n)

$A \rightarrow B_1$ and/or B_2 and/or B_3... and/or B_n

Parallel
The occurrence of one of a number of risks $(A_1, A_2,...,A_n)$ may cause the occurrence of one or more dependent risk events $(B_1, B_2,...,B_n)$.

A_1 or A_2... or $A_n \rightarrow B_1$ and/or B_2... and/or B_n

Series
The occurrence of a number of risk events together $(A_1, A_2,...,A_n)$ may cause the occurrence of one or more dependent risk events $(B_1, B_2,...,B_n)$.

A_1 and/or A_2... and/or $A_n \rightarrow B_1$ and/or B_2... and/or B_n

The simple model outlined above also assumes that it is possible to assign precise numerical probabilities to each of the risk events. These factors are, however, very often assessed subjectively. For example, if the project documentation is poor then it might be considered that there is *high* probability of time and cost overruns; alternatively, on the basis of past experience we might consider that there is a *low* probability of late payment by the client. It may be difficult to assign specific numbers to this kind of information, and in this case a 'fuzzy logic' approach, which attempts to quantify subjective data (Zadeh, 1965), would be useful. One possible approach is reported in Paek *et al.* (1993), but there is plainly a fertile area here for future research.

12.5   ASPECTS OF HUMAN DECISION-MAKING

It has already been shown that there is reason to believe that the majority of risk assessment decisions in construction are made intuitively and subjectively. The decision-making process during the estimating stage may therefore, in itself, give rise to additional risks and uncertainties in the tendering process. Mak and Raftery (1992) examined the tendering and estimating processes and concluded that the attendant risks and uncertainties fell into two distinct groups:

1. Risks and uncertainties arising from the cognitive processes of human beings; the use of common approximations and the individual's attitude towards taking risks.

2. The extent to which the decision-makers tend to attempt to reduce uncertainty and, to some extent risk, by making simplifying assumptions that may be unrealistic, in other words the tendency to assume away those real world uncertainties that we cannot objectively quantify.

These two groups are very difficult to separate, and both may be present in typical human decision-making. It might therefore be useful, in understanding the estimating and tendering processes, to consider briefly some aspects of human decision-making under conditions of uncertainty. Tversky and Khaneman (1986) concluded that people make decisions primarily on the basis of largely unstated beliefs and preferences, bearing in mind the context in which the decision is being made. They also conclude that:

People rely on a limited number of heuristic principles which reduce the complex tasks of assessing probabilities and predicting values to simpler judgemental operations.

In other words, as found by Mak and Raftery, people tend to assume away the things that they either do not understand or cannot objectively quantify.

Tversky and Khaneman identified three major types of heuristic knowledge typically used in subjective decision-making:

1. *Representative heuristics:* Probabilities are evaluated according to the degree that the problem matches other relevant experience.

2. *Availability heuristics:* Probabilities are assessed based on the ease with which similar events are brought to mind, in other words recent relevant experience has a strong bearing on current decision-making.

3. *Adjustment and anchoring heuristics:* People 'anchor' their estimates to some starting value, which they then use to make future estimates by adjustment from the anchor value. The adjustments are usually insufficient because people tend to try to rationalise new events to fit their existing frames of reference. In other words, they make simplifying assumptions to tie new events into things which they already understand.

It is also likely that people's attitudes towards taking decisions which involve risk and uncertainty, such as the forecasting of a construction price, will change over time, depending upon factors such as the penalty or reward which will result from an incorrect forecast and their own 'built-in' psychological attitude towards uncertain events. There is a considerable body of management research looking at the psychological factors that affect personal decision-making, from which it would appear that people are very inconsistent in the way they make decisions. Birnie and Yates (1991) give a useful summary of some of the psychological factors involved, but there is some evidence to suggest that the forecasts of time and cost made in the estimating process largely depend upon the estimator's attitude to the risks involved, in other words, the estimator's tendency to gamble. It therefore follows that a contractor attempting to fix the mark-up to convert an estimate into a tender will need some knowledge of the way in which the risks in the estimating process have been handled by the estimator: the contractor needs to know how much of a gambler the estimator is.

A number of techniques for the analysis of personal risk attitudes have been developed through research in psychology, business and management. The best known involve the use of *utility theory* to construct a graphical representation of personal risk attitude. The process basically works by asking the subject to choose between trading a guaranteed sum now for some larger uncertain sum in the future. For example, if you have a lottery ticket with a 50% chance of winning £100 000 how much would you sell it for? Someone who is 'risk neutral' might not be prepared to sell for less than £50 000; a 'risk taker' on the other hand might take the view that he or she would want more, and someone who is 'risk averse' might be prepared to take less. The results from a number of such questions are used to calculate a range of 'utility values', which are then plotted on a graph to show degrees of risk aversion. Ruegg and Marshall (1990, p. 211) explain the technique in detail.

Although research seems to show that the majority of business decision-makers are 'risk averse', that is, conservative in their decision-making, it may be useful in the tendering process for managers to know just how risk averse their estimators are.

The decision-making process can be improved by the application of formal decision analysis techniques. While a full discussion of this topic is beyond the scope of this text, Raiffa (1968, p. 271) summarises the best known technique well:

> The spirit of decision analysis is divide and conquer. Decompose a complex problem into smaller problems, get your thoughts straight in these simpler problems, paste them together with logical glue and come out with a program for action for the complex problem.

In other words, isolate each of the risks and uncertainties, understand the relationship between them and solve them one at a time. Note, however, that Ravinder *et al.* (1988) have shown that a definite limit exists for the decomposition; that is, there comes a point at which it is not productive to break the problem down any further.

12.6   RISKS AND UNCERTAINTIES TO BE CONSIDERED IN THE ESTIMATING PROCESS

The risks and uncertainties faced by the contractor in the estimating process may be divided into three distinct groups:

1. Risks posed by the project itself

2. Risks posed by the professional team

3. Risks implicit in the contractor's own estimating process

The first two groups may be to some extent unique to each project, but the third group has an effect on every estimate the company prepares.

12.6.1   Project Risk

A number of different risks are posed by various aspects of the project and the associated procurement and contractual approaches. All of these risks are interrelated and must be considered together. Risks posed by the project might include those described below.

Procurement Methodology and Proposed Contractual Arrangement
Different procurement methodologies and contractual arrangements pose different degrees of risk for the contractor, and the contract documents will normally attempt to spell out and allocate the balance of risks between the parties in an attempt to control the consequences of risky and uncertain events. As McGowan *et al.* (1992) point out:

> The principal purpose of the contract is to define how the risk is to be shared between the client and the contractor.

Unfortunately, in the case of most of the commonly used Standard Forms of Contract, attempts to provide contractual mechanisms to control and limit the effects of risky events, largely as a result of developments through the courts in the law of contract, have resulted in Standard Forms of Contract becoming increasingly complex and bulky. This approach has been seen by some as an exercise in damage limitation, in that it simply attempts to provide remedies for the occurrence of an increasingly large number of events within the framework of the contract rather than through the courts, an attempt to close the legal door after the contractual horse has bolted rather than a positive attempt to improve both parties' prospects for success, particularly for major projects. Some commentators (see for example Macneil (1974) and Campbell and Harris (1993)), have argued powerfully that the underlying problems of long-term contracts can only be solved by a completely new approach to the construction of contracts for major projects aimed at developing a partnership between the client and the contractor based on a 'win/win' scenario rather than the confrontational approach adopted in the past.

Be that as it may, the main problem from the contractor's point of view is that for many, perhaps most, competitively tendered projects, the procurement methodology and contractual conditions are established unilaterally by the client long before the contractor becomes involved, and they will often be aimed at minimising the risk from the client's point of view. Since, as already established, all projects, no matter how well planned, will always contain some element of risk, minimising the risk for the client can all too easily mean placing the main share of the risk with the contractor.

As far as individual procurement routes are concerned, it is difficult to be precise about which are more risky than others and to what extent, simply because of all of the different risks involved. In general terms, however, it is apparent, for example, that a contractor is almost certain to be faced with less risk on a cost reimbursement project than on a project based on unit rates, and similar findings would apply to projects including a fluctuations adjustment clause rather than those based on a fixed price. In the case of projects based on variants of the design and build model, the contractor carries considerable risk for the design, the price and the time-scale, but at least has control of all of the inputs. So far as lump sum contracts are concerned, Ireland (1987) has commentated that:

> The maximum possible risk to the contractor occurs in the lump sum contract in which the extent of the work is only moderately well specified and the cost of the work is tendered for without possible change. If prices rise due to inflation, or if the time of construction is significantly lengthened due to industrial action, poor weather or shortage of materials, the contractor is severely disadvantaged.

Adequacy of the Project Information Upon Which the Tender is to Be Based
Pressure of time, often imposed by clients of the industry, means that by far the greatest majority of construction projects are put to tender before all of the drawings and schedules necessary for construction are complete. Note that this comment does not refer to minor pieces of information – even on the best projects it would not, for example, be expected that colour schedules would be completed at tender stage. Items falling under this heading are substantial pieces of missing information which would be likely to have a significant effect on the contractor's price. It is not, for example, unknown for contractors to be expected to tender for quite complex works on the basis of little more then 1:100 scale plans and elevations. Teo *et al.* (1991), discussing their survey of 47 UK contractors engaged in refurbishment work, comment that:

> The primary factor underlying variability of tenders for refurbishment work lies in the unsuitability of the tender documentation, which often fails to convey the scope and extent of the work. This leads risk averse contractors to include hidden contingency sums in their tenders to allow for risk. Risk seeking contractors, on the other hand, seize the opportunity to reduce their tenders by the scope of the potential for claims within the tender documents.

It has already been shown that, on complex construction projects, the contractor will need to plan the construction carefully before submitting a tender. In particular, the calculation of preliminaries costs will require the preparation of detailed method statements and operational plans. Obviously, the less complete the project information the more difficult it is for the contractor to plan the work and thus be reasonably certain that the final estimate will bear a reasonable relationship to the out-turn costs if it gets the job. Incomplete information at tender stage also implies a high risk of variations during the course of the work. Such variations are generally regarded as bad news for a contractor working to a tight programme. They are disruptive and expensive, and the way that some Conditions of Contract are interpreted by some consultants means that contractors sometimes complain that they are not fully reimbursed for the true costs involved.

Contractors therefore need to look closely at the information provided by the architect and engineers. Beware of the bills of quantities. Remember that the bills can only be as accurate as the information provided to the quantity surveyor. If projects are not fully detailed when the quantities are prepared it is likely that the quantity surveyor may include some measured items for work not shown on the drawings but which he or she thinks is likely to be required in order to try to make sure that the tender sum is high enough to cover the cost of the work required. There is nothing inherently wrong with this approach provided the bill makes clear that this is what has been done by marking the items as 'PROVISIONAL' (in other words the contractor is made aware that these items have not been accurately measured because sufficient information is not available). Unfortunately, it is not unknown for some architects to expect quantity surveyors to make up their own details for things yet to be designed, and to pass this information off as fact. Burridge (1994) is splendidly eloquent on this point:

> For some reason QSs see it as part of their job to produce a convincing 100 page bill of quantities from a sketch on the back of a table napkin, and then wonder why so many projects end in dispute, late and over budget.

Alternatively, the bills may include 'PROVISIONAL SUMS' (i.e. lump sums of money which all contractors are required to include in their tenders to cover work which has yet to be designed).

Project Time-scale and Penalties for Non-completion

As discussed in Chapter 5, contractors will need to make an assessment of the available project time-scales, both for the preparation of the tender and also for completion of the construction works. The construction time-scale allowed by the client should be compared with the contractor's proposed programme, and an assessment should be made of the likelihood of the project being completed on time together with the likely losses and penalties in the event of failure. On most construction contracts the potential consequences of failure to complete on time will usually include payments from the contractor to the client in the form of liquidated and ascertained damages. The relevant figures will be set out in the bill of quantities, and the contractor can therefore make an assessment of the likely consequences of late completion.

Note that in some Forms of Contract the client has discretion as to whether or not it invokes the liquidated damages clause, and the contractor will therefore also need to assess how likely it is that the client will apply them. Some contracts include a bonus for early completion, and this will also need to be considered. Some contracts not only require that the contractor complete the whole project on time, but also that it must achieve predefined programme milestones. Failure to hit the milestone dates may incur severe financial penalties, which may then cause the contractor considerable difficulty with the rest of the project. A good understanding of the Contract Conditions is thus required in order that reliable assessments of the risks may be made.

Fixed or Fluctuating Price

Construction contracts may be let on either a 'fixed price' or a 'fluctuating price' basis. Fluctuating price means that the contractor is required to submit a bid based on prices ruling at the date of tender, and the contractor will be reimbursed for the cost effect of any price rises which occur as a result of inflation during the course of the contract. A fixed price, on the other hand, means that the contractor is required to make an assessment of the likely effects of price inflation, generally excluding increases caused as a result of tax and levy changes, during the contract period and to make due allowance in the price. Note that both 'fixed price' and 'fluctuating price' contracts are adjustable for the costs of any variations that occur. Fixed price contracts therefore impose an additional risk on the contractor in that the tender must include a forecast of the likely effect of future price increases during the contract period. The extent of the risk obviously increases with the length of the contract period, and also in times of high inflation.

Level of Prime Cost Sums

The contractor has virtually no price risk associated with any work for which prime cost sums are included in the bills. Prime cost sums are sums of money which all contractors are required to include in their tender for works to be carried out or materials to be supplied by specialists appointed by the client and its advisors, and for which the client will effectively carry the price risk. In other words, if the prime cost sums fail to cover the actual costs of the work, the difference will effectively be paid by the client, not by the contractor. The level of prime cost sums is therefore of interest to the contractor in assessing its price risk – generally, the higher the proportion of prime cost sums in the project the lower the risk to the contractor as far as the overall price is concerned.

On the other hand, the contractor does have the responsibility for controlling and coordinating the work of all of the specialist subcontractors working on the project, and this will include all of the work covered by the prime cost sums. It is likely that at the time the tender is prepared many of the specialists will not have been appointed. The contractor therefore has the difficult problem of including in its programme possibly large amounts of work, some of which may be on the critical path, to be carried out by an unknown specialist. The various Conditions of Contract have differing provisions for the letting of work which is the subject of prime cost sums, giving the contractor varying degrees of control. In some cases, for example the JCT80 Standard Form of Building Contract, the contract makes provision for the main contractor and the nominated subcontractor to agree relevant programme dates as part of the subcontractor's tendering process, but in other forms the nominated subcontractor is simply appointed by the architect, often on the basis of the architect's perception of when the work is required to be done, and the contractor has to cope as best it can. From this point of view, therefore, a high level of prime cost sums may be a distinct disadvantage. It is therefore not only the level of prime cost sums that is important, but also the Conditions of Contract and the degree to which the specialist firms have been appointed at the time of the main contractor's tender.

Degree of Technological Difficulty

The contractor needs to consider factors such as how difficult the project will be to construct, whether the technology is new or well-tried, and how serious the consequences are if things do not go as planned. In general, the newer the technology the higher the risk. Unfortunately, it appears that these risks are frequently underestimated. Holman and Keizer (1994) believe that:

> Disappointment and failures in the realisation of product innovation projects are often due to a naïve but optimistic attitude towards a perceived gap between available and required knowledge and skills.

For major projects with a high degree of technological innovation contractors would be well advised to conduct a formal risk assessment and evaluation. Holman and Keizer discuss the development of a risk diagnosis and management (RDM) methodology which, although originally devised for use in manufacturing, could equally well be applied to construction. Risk assessment is therefore intimately connected with the preparation of project planning studies and method statements. Good computer-based planning systems include the opportunity to include at least three durations for each activity, namely most likely, highest likely and lowest likely times, and the use of simulations using packages of this type can be very useful in the assessment of technological risks.

12.6.2 Risks Posed by the Client and the Professional Team

As far as the client is concerned, the main problem from the contractor's point of view arises from uncertainty about whether or not it will be paid on time.

It has already been shown that cash flow is of fundamental importance to any contractor, and late payment by the client will mean that the contractor has to finance the works to a greater extent than originally envisaged when the tender was submitted. This is likely to have potentially serious effects upon the profitability of the contract. Although the Conditions of Contract will include clear and unambiguous provisions for interim payments, the contractor is to a large extent reliant on the client for prompt payment, and if the client is consistently late with payments there is in reality not a lot the contractor can do. Once construction work has been completed it cannot easily be disassembled again. The contractor could, where the contract conditions permit, determine the contract, or alternatively sue for breach, or even, in extreme cases, abandon the works, but none of these options is likely to recover outstanding monies quickly and few contractors will want to take such radical steps unless it appears that the client is never going to pay at all. It is therefore important that the contractor evaluates this risk carefully before submitting a tender.

A further uncertainty arises in the stringency with which the members of the professional team are likely to interpret the Conditions of Contract. Although in most cases the wording of the contract may be perfectly clear, the words may be subject to varying interpretations by different consultants. Some of the major problems faced by the contractor are described below.

Interim Valuations not Reflecting the True Cost of the Work

Consultant quantity surveyors sometimes see themselves as guardians of the client's financial interest, and there is therefore a temptation to tend towards keeping the value of interim valuations low in order to make sure that the client would not be financially exposed if the contractor were to go into liquidation. While the shortfall might not appear large on a particular contract, and the under-valuation will in any case sort itself out once the contract is completed, an under-valuation in interim certificates of, say, 2.5% on all of the projects the contractor is working on can pose very serious cash flow problems. The contractor is entitled to the full value of all work properly completed at the time of each valuation, less only the retention percentage stipulated in the contract, and in extreme cases of undervaluation could sue the relevant consultant (quantity surveyor, engineer or architect) for professional negligence. In practice, of course, this will only be a very last resort, and most contractors will try other means to influence the valuation. One common way in which contractors try to ensure that the valuation includes the full value of all work completed is for the contractor to offer to prepare the valuation itself and then to submit it to the consultant for checking. Although it is usually spelled out, at least in building contracts, that the responsibility for preparing the valuation rests with the quantity surveyor, some consultants are prepared to accept this method of working.

Payment for Variations not Fully Reflecting the True Cost of the Work
All Standard Conditions of Contract will include clear rules for the valuation of variations. In the normal standard forms of building contract the contractual philosophy is to try to ensure that the additional payment for variations reflects the pricing level in the original tender, and the principal method of achieving this is to require, wherever possible, variations to be priced either at the rates set out in the tender bills or at rates derived from those quoted in the tender. Most contracts provide for other alternative methods of valuation if it can be shown that the varied work is executed under special conditions, but it is usually clear from the contract wording that the main basis for valuation is intended to be the rates in the tender bill, and quantity surveyors vary greatly in their willingness to move away from valuation at bill rates. Since, in most contracts, the final responsibility for valuation of variations rests with either the quantity surveyor or with the engineer, there is again usually little the contractor can do officially if negotiation fails, short of arbitration or legal action.

Delay in Completion of the Final Account
Most consultant quantity surveyors earn most of their fees from pre-contract work, and final accounts for completed projects tend to be set aside in favour of work on new commissions. Clients do not usually object to this, since, once the building is completed, they see no need to make further payments to the builder before they have to. Things have improved in recent times. In the bad old days it was common for the final account not to be completed until several years after completion of the project itself. It may be that the balance outstanding is relatively small, but again the financial consequences of having a large number of final accounts outstanding have in the past been enough to drive some contractors into bankruptcy. The risk must be evaluated on the basis of past experience or the consultant's reputation.

Architect's/Engineer's/Clerk of Works Interpretation of the Specification
The quality standards clauses in many specifications are often loose and ambiguous. Wording such as 'Workmanship and materials shall be of the best quality obtainable' is subject to considerable degrees of interpretation, and architects, engineers and clerks of works vary greatly in their interpretation of quality standards, and thus their acceptance or otherwise of completed work. An architect who has extremely demanding standards of quality, and who thus regularly condemns borderline standard work, will have an obvious and considerable effect on progress and therefore on the contractor's profitability. This factor is likely to be closely associated with the type of project, and the contractor must therefore assess this risk in the light of the particular combination of project and consultants.

12.6.3   Risks and Uncertainties Inherent in the Contractor's Tendering and Estimating Process

Having considered the risks posed by the project and by the professional team, it is also necessary to consider the risks and uncertainties inherent in the contractor's own estimating process. It has already been shown that, in any project, the estimating process requires the estimating team to make a number of assumptions (for example about work rates, anticipated weather conditions and price stability), and each of these assumptions has associated with it some element of risk or uncertainty. These assumptions are a fundamental part of the process of making any forecast, and their associated risks are rarely quantified. In effect, they represent the everyday decisions that professional estimators are paid to take; indeed, it could be argued that they constitute the very essence of the estimator's professional skill. Note also that although many modern contractors attempt to reduce some of these risks by letting extensive parts of the work out to domestic subcontractors, they cannot subcontract the risks entirely. Even in cases of extensive domestic subcontracting, the main contractor is still responsible for planning the works, for pricing the preliminaries element and for arranging any necessary financing. In addition, where work is let to a domestic subcontractor, the main contractor also takes the risk that the subcontractor will actually complete the work within the required time-scales and to the required quality standards. Do not forget that, as far as the contract with the client is concerned, the main contractor takes full responsibility for the work of all of its domestic subcontractors. It can be seen therefore that although subcontracting large parts of the project can ease the risk as far as price is concerned, it can add additional risks in other areas.

It has also been shown that the decisions made by estimators are affected partly by their levels of confidence in their own professional competence, and also by their own personal attitudes to risk. It is therefore totally unrealistic to consider an estimator's prediction of likely cost as a single-point figure, although this is apparently what management wishes to do. An estimator's prediction is in fact only one value drawn from a probability distribution of possible costs, and it must be recognised that the single-point value chosen by the estimator will depend largely upon the estimator's own psychological state at the time the decision is made. The estimator will be heavily influenced by, among other things, a personal assessment of reprimand or reward if the figure is not accurate. If, for example, the estimator believes that censure will follow if the project is won but the estimate is shown to be low, the estimator will tend to choose a value from the high end of the likely range of cost, whereas if he or she has been told to 'sharpen your pencil' then the choice may be from the low end of the range. These perceptions are personal and will change over time. The key therefore is to try to reduce the estimator's consideration of reprimand or reward, in order to ensure firstly that estimates are consistently produced on the same basis, but secondly that the estimator always gives the most likely and unbiased assessment of likely project cost backed up by lowest practical and highest likely values.

12.7   CONCLUSIONS

It can clearly be seen that the processes of tendering and estimating are subject to considerable degrees of risk and uncertainty, and it is also evident that contractors can both increase their chances of winning competitive tenders and remove some of the uncertainty involved in making the required profits if they have a better understanding of the causes and effects of the uncertainties involved.

Perhaps the most important lesson to learn is that it is totally unrealistic for managers to continue to consider estimates for construction work in terms of single-point figures. It has been shown that the evaluation and quantification of risk and uncertainty ought to involve consideration of the probabilities that various outcomes may occur. The use of range estimates incorporated within a probability distribution may therefore lead to better decision-making at the tender stage.

Business and management research has developed a range of tools to aid risk analysis and decision-making, and these are well documented in the literature, but there seems to be little evidence of their use in construction at present. The risks and uncertainties identified here fall into several different groups, and the evaluation of each might require the use of different tools. The question of risks and uncertainties arising from the competitive market-place will be considered in the next chapter.

12.8   REFERENCES

Berny J. and Townsend P.R.F. (1993) 'Macrosimulation of project risks – a practical way forward', *International Journal of Project Management*, Vol. 11, No. 4, pp. 201–8.

Birnie J. and Yates A. (1991) 'Cost prediction using decision/risk analysis methodologies', *Construction Management and Economics*, April 1991, pp. 171–86.

Blake E.H. (1900) 'Extras and omissions in building contracts' *The Surveyors Institution Transactions*, Vol. XXXII, pp. 525–72.

Bowers J.A. (1994) 'Data for project risk analysis', *International Journal of Project Management*, Vol. 12, No. 1, pp. 17–22.

Burridge B. (1994) 'Estimate or guestimate', *Chartered Builder*, June, pp. 18–19.

Campbell D. and Harris D. (1993) Flexibility in long term contractual relationships; the role of co-operation, *Journal of Law and Society*, Vol. 20, No. 2.

Fine B. (1987) 'Kitchen sink economics and the construction industry', in *Building, Cost Modelling and Computers*, (ed. Brandon P.S.), E. & F.N. Spon, London.

Hillebrandt P.M. (1974) *Economic Theory and the Construction Industry*, Macmillan, London.

Holman J.I.M. and Keizer J.A. (1994) 'Diagnosing risks in product innovative projects', *International Journal of Project Management*, Vol. 12, No. 2, pp. 75–80.

Ireland V. (1987) 'The choice of contractual arrangement', in *Proceedings, Project Managers National Conference*, Adelaide, Australia.

Mak S. and Raftery J. (1992) 'Risk attitude and systematic bias in estimating and forecasting', *Construction Management and Economics*, July 1992, pp. 303–20.

Kangari R. (1991) 'Construction business failure and risk management in the USA', in *Management, Quality and Economics in Building*, (eds. Bezalga A. and Brandon P.), E. & F.N. Spon, London.

Macneil I.R. (1974) 'The many futures of contracts', *Southern California Law Review*, Vol. 47, pp. 691–816.

McGowan P.H., Malcolm R., Horner W., Jones D. and Thompson P.A. (1992) *Allocation and evaluation of risk in construction contracts*, Occasional Paper No. 52, Chartered Institute of Building, London.

Paek J.H., Lee Y.W. and Ock J.H. (1993) 'Pricing construction risk: fuzzy set application', *Journal of Construction Engineering and Management*, Vol. 119, No. 4.

Raiffa H. (1968) *Decision analysis: Introductory Lectures on Choices and Uncertainty*, Addison-Wesley, Reading MA.

Ravinder H.V., Kleinmuntz D.W. and Dyar J.S. (1988) 'The reliability of subjective probabilities obtained through decomposition', *Management Science*, Vol. 34, No. 2, pp. 306–12.

Ren H. (1994) 'Risk lifecycle and risk relationships on construction projects', *International Journal of Project Management*, Vol. 12, No. 2, pp. 68–74.

Rowe W.D. (1977) *An Anatomy of Risk*, Wiley-Interscience, New York.

Ruegg R.T. and Marshall H.E. (1990) *Building Economics Theory and Practice*, Van Nostrand Reinhold, New York.

Senior G. (1990) *Risk and Uncertainty in Lump Sum Contracts*, Technical Information Service No. 113, Chartered Institute of Building, London.

Tah J.H.M., Thorpe A. and McCaffer R. (1994) 'A survey of indirect cost estimating in practice', *Construction Management and Economics*, Vol. 12, pp. 31–6.

Teo D.H.P., Quah L.K., Torrance V.B. and Okoro M.I. (1991) 'Risk evaluation and decision support system for tendering and bidding in refurbishment contracts', in *Management, Quality and Economics in Building* (eds. Bezalga A. and Brandon P.S.), E. & F.N. Spon, London.

Tversky A. and Khaneman D. (1986) 'Judgement under uncertainty: heuristics and biases', in *Judgement and Decision Making* (Arkes H.R. and Hammond K.R.), Cambridge University Press, Cambridge MA.

Williams T.M. (1994) 'Using a risk register to integrate risk management in project definition', *International Journal of Project Management*, Vol. 12, No. 1, pp. 17–22.

Zadeh L.A. (1965) 'Fuzzy sets', *Information and Control*, Vol. 8, No. 3, pp. 338–53.

13 Bidding Strategies

13.1 INTRODUCTION

Chapter 12 considered some of the basic theory of risk analysis and discussed the risks that might affect the estimating process. This chapter examines the risks of the construction market-place, the decisions the contractor must take when tendering in competition, and the techniques available to contractors in the assessment of their mark-up in formulating their bid price.

13.2 THE TENDERING PROCESS

From the contractor's point of view, the tendering process begins with the invitation to tender. While contractors' willingness to tender for any particular scheme will depend to some extent on the amount of work around, under normal circumstances it is generally believed that building contractors do not usually submit a truly competitive tender for every project that comes along. Although few contractors will actually decline an invitation, they must still make a policy decision about whether to submit a *bona fide* tender. Available resources will dictate that they must be selective, choosing which work they will tender for from a continually changing array of potential projects. Upon receipt of the tender enquiry, therefore, a contractor must decide whether to accept the invitation to submit a price for the work or to decline. If the invitation is accepted, the contractor will prepare and submit a price for the work. In legal terms, the price represents an offer which, if accepted by the client, will constitute the basis for a binding contract.

It is therefore evident that the contractor is faced with two crucial decisions: firstly whether or not to submit a competitive tender, and if so what the bid price should be.

13.3 ACCEPTANCE OR REJECTION?

The decision whether or not to submit a *bona fide* tender is obviously of crucial importance to the contractor. It has already been shown that a considerable part of the industry's workload is let by competitive tender, and it is therefore by submission of successful tenders that the contractor will secure most of its income. In short, 'if you aren't in you can't win!'. It might therefore be reasonable to start from the premise that, in a normal trading climate, a contractor might tend towards acceptance of an invitation unless there are good reasons for not doing so. The problem is of course that, even when work in the industry is scarce, the flow of enquiries is not regular, and few contractors will have the resources to respond positively to all of the enquiries they receive. In addition, the decision to submit a *bona fide* tender commits the contractor to some expenditure in the preparation of an estimate (in the case of a large project to considerable expenditure), which will not be recovered if the bid is unsuccessful.

Contractors therefore need to examine each enquiry carefully and decide how they should respond. It has been suggested (Ansoff, 1965) that the contractor has five possible courses of action open:

1. Reject the project

2. Provisionally accept the project

3. Add it to a reserve list

4. Remove a project from the reserve list and replace it with the current project

5. Unconditional acceptance

Skitmore (1989), however, points out that in practice the limited time available for tendering restricts contractors' use of reserve lists, and the usual options are simply acceptance or rejection. Note, however, that rejection may not mean that the contractor does not submit a bid. Where the client is influential in the industry or has a regular programme of work, it is possible that contractors may feel that they will prejudice their chances of future enquiries if they reject a tender enquiry outright. In this case, contractors may accept the invitation to tender even though they have already decided that they are not interested in the work. The usual approach is to submit a 'cover price'.

In practice, the decision about whether to submit a tender or not will depend upon a number of factors to do with the present and forecast future state of the contractor's business at the time. The CIOB (1983) suggests that the decision will be taken largely on basis of the type of work involved (i.e. whether it fits into one of the categories in which the company has expertise), together with availability of the necessary resources both to prepare the estimate and to carry out the work, whereas other authors postulate that the key factors in the decision will be the contractor's present workload and/or the availability of key personnel.

Table 13.1 Factors influencing project selection (Odusote and Fellows, 1992)

1. Client-related factors
2. Type of work
3. Value of the project
4. Contractor's current workload
5. Estimating workload
6. Likely profitability of the contract
7. Location of the project
8. Form of contract
9. Physical resources to do the job
10. Identity of consultants
11. Time available to tender

Note: Factors 1 and 2 identified as the most important by approximately 75% of the sample. Remainder of factors each identified as most important by less than 50% of the sample.

In truth, there has been comparatively little objective research done on the factors that influence a contractor's decision in any particular case.

A UK study by Odusote and Fellows (1992) reviewed the literature and listed 42 separate considerations identified by 17 other authors as being important in the project selection process. They then used the data from the literature search to formulate a questionnaire survey of UK-based building contractors, each with a turnover of £8 m per year or more. 48 companies replied to the survey, and the most important factors identified in the survey, ranked in order of importance, are shown in Table 13.1.

On the other hand, an American study by Ahmad and Minkarah (1988) identified 31 factors affecting the bidding decisions of top US contractors, and this list was used in a later study conducted by Shash (1990) involving a questionnaire survey of leading British contractors. Shash asked the contractors to consider and rank a list of 55 possible factors which might affect the 'bid/no bid' decision. The results, based on a sample of 80 contractors, were then produced as a table, and the 'top 20' factors, identified as most important by more than 60% of the sample, ranked in order, are shown in Table 13.2.

As one might expect, there is some level of agreement between the two studies on the *identity* of the major factors considered to be significant in the bid/no bid decision, even if there is little agreement about their relative *importance*. In the light of previous discussions about the way people make decisions, it would in any case seem highly unlikely that *every* contractor would consider *all* of these points for *every* tender enquiry received. It would seem much more likely that *some* contractors might consider *some* of these factors on *some* jobs, and that different factors might be considered by

Table 13.2 Factors affecting project selection (Shash, 1990)

1.   Contractors' need for work
2.   Number of competitors tendering
3.   Experience in similar projects
4.   Current work load
5.   Owner/client identity
6.   Contract conditions
7.   Project type
8.   Past profit in similar projects
9.   Project size
10. Tendering method (selective/open)
11. Risk owing to the nature of the work
12. Project location
13. Type of contract
14. Availability of qualified staff
15. Rate of return
16. Project cash flow
17. Tender period
18. Availability of other projects
19. Availability of labour
20. Completeness of the documents

different contractors for each new project, that is, the contractor makes a set of intuitive and subjective judgements about each new project in the light of its own prevailing circumstances at the time. The search for a definitive list of factors might therefore have something of the character of a search for the Holy Grail. However, the contention that the contractor's need for the work is one of the most important issues in the bid/no bid decision is supported by American experience reported by Griffis (1992), who writes that:

> ...this author has found that volume [of work] on hand... is a major influence on the utility that a building contractor places on particular bid letting.

Remember, however, that Hillebrandt (1974) contends that the need for work should be judged according to whether the firm is on the downward, constant or upward slope of its cost curve.

Perhaps all that can be said with any accuracy is that the bid/no bid decision is a dynamic and very complex one, and there is some evidence (Odusote and Fellows, 1992) that, for a large project, it is likely that the decisions will be made by a group of people rather than one individual.

Some commentators, however, have suggested that contractors can reduce their overall risk exposure by choosing the projects that they wish to actively tender for such that they hold a diversified portfolio of projects. This contention is built on financial portfolio theory, which basically says that investors can afford to hold some risky investments if those investments are balanced in the overall portfolio by other less risky ones. Proponents of the theory in construction hold that inherently risky projects can be undertaken in some safety provided that they are balanced by less risky ones. Kangari and Riggs (1988) summarise the position, and point out that there are significant difficulties in applying the approach to construction. They conclude that diversification of the project portfolio can generally reduce but not eliminate overall risk exposure.

13.4 SETTING THE BID PRICE

Assuming that the contractor has decided to submit a *bona fide* tender, the second key decision the contractor must make is the level of the bid price. It has already been shown that contractors will normally base their bid price on an estimate of the cost of the inputs to the process. Once the estimate is complete the process of compiling the tender bid is a management activity. The tender represents the contractor's offer to carry out the work, and might be defined as 'The sum of money, time and other conditions required by the tenderer to carry out the work'. The management process involved in converting the estimate into a tender is called adjudication.

Considerable research has been carried out over a period of some 40 years into the ways in which contractors can improve their chances of submitting the 'best' bid. Different approaches have included the attempted development of various mathematical models of the bidding process, methods based on historical data, statistical bidding models, and models based on econometric techniques. Other researchers (see for example Al-Tabtabai and Diekman (1992)) have taken a less mathematical approach, generally based on attempting to analyse the human decision-making process as it applies to forecasting.

Moselhi *et al.* (1993), however, maintain that:

Markup estimation is a decision problem that is so highly unstructured that it is difficult to analyse and formulate an adequate solution mechanism. It is both time consuming and complicated to identify all the related factors that form a rational basis for such decisions, analyse their individual strengths, and then quantify their combined impact on the decision. The usual practice is to make bid decisions on the basis of intuition, derived from a mixture of gut feeling, experience and guesses. This implies some sort of pattern recognition is used rather than computation or deep reasoning about the problem elements.

They go on to present a computer-based decision support system called DBID, using a neural network technique which they then demonstrate through an example.

The present situation regarding research in this area is eloquently summed up by Park and Chapin (1992, p. 197):

> Many different theoretical approaches to competitive bidding have been proposed and tested with varying results. Any of these strategies should improve the contractor's bidding effectiveness, and whichever one works best for a particular competitive situation is obviously the best one to use. It will be worth whatever time is required to at least become familiar with the different approaches; they all offer some good ideas, and even a bad plan is better than no plan at all.

Perhaps the first stage in trying to understand the process is to try to review:

1. The factors generally taken into account by contractors during the bidding process

2. The information normally considered to be necessary for the bidding process to be carried out

13.5   FACTORS GENERALLY CONSIDERED BY CONTRACTORS WHEN BIDDING

We have already seen that, in crude terms, the bid price for construction work will include the total of the net estimate with appropriate additions for overheads, profit and risk margin.

Most of the components of the bid may therefore be estimated with some degree of accuracy. The net estimate is provided by the estimator together with notes detailing how any risks identified in the estimating process have been dealt with, and the overheads budget and required baseline profit are generally set for the year by the firm's business plan. The only item therefore left for consideration is the risk margin: the contractor's assessment of the special risks and/or the commercial attractiveness presented by this particular project.

Having said, then, that the adjudication process is essentially about getting the job at the best possible price, it would be useful to look at the factors that contractors might consider when assessing the project's risk margin and thus setting the tender bid. Eastham (1987), reviewing the state of research in this area, reported that he could find no objective research, although his literature review did identify 90 individual factors *thought* to influence the tender price. Further research, however, in the form of unstructured interviews conducted

Table 13.3 Factors affecting bid levels (Eastham, 1987)

1. Subcontract requirements
2. Type and size of job
3. Competitors
4. Client and professionals
5. Labour requirements

with estimators working with 10 contractors in the north of England, revealed that only five factors (see Table 13.3) were identified by all 10 estimators, and that these did not correlate well with those factors thought to be most important by the authors studied in his literature review.

Shash (1990) also examined the factors that contractors take into account when formulating their tender bids, through the medium of a structured questionnaire. Those factors identified as most important by more than 60% of the respondents, ranked in order, are shown in Table 13.4.

Teo *et al.* (1991) report on a study of 47 refurbishment contractors in the UK, and the factors identified in their survey are shown in Table 13.5. They further comment that closer examination of the responses shows that most contractors tend to place more emphasis on personal relationships when adjudicating their tenders. The least important factors were found to be those relating to general market and political conditions.

In this case factors such as the number of competitors tendering and the perceived competitiveness of competitors were ranked comparatively low, being considered very important by only slightly more than 40% of the companies surveyed. It would therefore appear that in many companies the decision on risk margin is a very subjective one, and this is supported by Shash's conclusion that less than 20% of the companies surveyed use any kind of mathematical or statistical tendering model. Shash also reported that while over 95% of the companies surveyed reported that they were happy with the way they make tendering decisions, two of the firms who used

Table 13.4 Factors affecting bidding conditions (Shash, 1990)

1. Degree of difficulty of the work
2. Risk owing to the nature of the work
3. Current workload
4. Need for the work
5. Contract conditions
6. Anticipated cost of liquidated damages
7. Owner/client identity
8. Past profit in similar work

Table 13.5 Factors affecting bidding (Teo et al., 1991)

1. Accuracy of contractor's cost estimate
2. Credit worthiness of client
3. Contractual liabilities
4. Type of job
5. Relationship with consultants
6. Relationship with clients
7. Workload commitment of contractor
8. Complexity of work
9. Size of job
10. Amendments to standard contract form

mathematical models to assist their tendering reported dissatisfaction with their tendering decisions.

Again there seems to be some measure of agreement among the three studies regarding the identity of the factors considered, but perhaps, as with the bid/no bid decision, the decision in this case is again a dynamic one where the factors considered vary over time from project to project and from firm to firm.

13.6 BIDDING MODELS

Given the estimator's prediction(s) of likely cost, having examined and evaluated, as far as is possible, all of the various risks and uncertainties implicit in the project, in the professional team and within the estimating function itself, and bearing in mind the general level of profit that it is necessary for the firm to make to keep the shareholders happy, the managers making the adjudication decision will have some idea of the range of mark-up figures which they consider it would be appropriate to apply to the specific project under consideration. They must then combine this information with their perception/intelligence of the market trends in order to reach the tender figure, and it would be sensible to assume that this process might be more successful more often given some knowledge, or at least prediction, of the way in which they expect their competitors to behave.

As has already been shown, a number of alternative techniques have been proposed over the course of the past 40 years to model the bidding process. In general, the value of the bid can be represented as:

Bid = Estimated cost + Mark-up

where the 'estimated cost' includes predicted total cost to the contractor, including overheads and financing charges, and 'mark-up' is composed of the contractor's profit and usually the contract risk premium. The majority of the research has concentrated on the development of 'bidding models' designed to find the 'best' mark-up value.

The major types of bidding model are:

1. Models based on probability theory

2. Regression models

3. Econometric models

A detailed review of the state of the art in statistical modelling is given in Chapter 7 of Skitmore (1989).

13.7   THE PROBABILITY APPROACH

Bidding models based on probability theory were first developed in the USA. The basic theory was developed by Friedman (1956), when he postulated that in a tender auction it was possible to model each bidder's behaviour as a function of the estimated cost by means of a probability distribution. Ioannou (1988) gives a good explanation of the application of Freidman's model in construction. Friedman's general approach was modified by a number of other researchers, and there have been several attempts to apply the theory specifically to the construction industry. The probability approach has histori-cally been the most popular technique for the construction of bidding models, and it is therefore worth examining the technique in some detail.

The general approach assumes that there are a number of bidders compet-ing regularly against each other in the same market-place. The theory then postulates that, given a sufficient number of opportunities to tender against known competitors, any one player can collect sufficient information to model the relationship between its own mark-up on future projects against the probability of submitting the lowest tender. The theory assumes that the basic prime cost of the scheme is similar for all tenderers, and that by comparing the company's competitors' tender figures for past projects with its own estimate of prime cost a contractor can therefore develop a probability distribution for each of its competitors, showing the likelihood of winning future tenders with different mark-ups. Note that it makes no difference how the prime cost is defined provided the cost is calculated in the same way for every job. Table 13.6 shows a typical example of the approach.

The above example gives the theoretical possibility of beating competitor A on future projects at varying levels of mark-up, but it does not help to decide which level of mark-up will be the best bet.

Friedman's original work tackled this point, and he postulated that the bidder's long-term main objective would be to maximise the expected level

Table 13.6 Example of simple probability model

First collect information about our performance against each of our competitors in the following way:

Comparison of bids submitted by competitor A with our prime cost

Contract No.	Own cost estimate (£)	A's bid (£)	Ratio col. 3:col. 2
1	10 000 000	11 400 000	1.14
2	6 000 000	7 200 000	1.20
3	24 200 000	26 100 000	1.07
4...			

Next convert the information into a frequency distribution. The following gives the information for a sample of 100 contracts:

Frequency of competitor A's bids

Ratio A: our cost	Number of times	Probability	Probability of beating A
0.91–1.00	1	0.01	1.00
1.01–1.10	5	0.05	0.99
1.11–1.20	14	0.14	0.94
1.21–1.30	28	0.28	0.80
1.31–1.40	35	0.35	0.52
1.41–1.50	14	0.14	0.17
over 1.50	3	0.03	0.03

(*Note:* Figures in column 4 are calculated by successively deducting the probability of a particular ratio from the previous line.)

If we are now bidding against competitor A we can assess our chances of success at various mark-up levels as follows:

Probability of beating competitor A

Mark-up (%)	Our bid:prime cost	Probability of beating A
−10	0.90	1.00
0	1.00	0.99
10	1.10	0.94
20	1.20	0.80
30	1.30	0.52
40	1.40	0.17
50	1.50	0.03

Table 13.7 Expected value of profits (single competitor)

Mark-up (%)	Probability of beating A	Expected profit (%)
−10	1.00	$-10 \times 1.00 = -10$
0	0.99	$0 \times 0.99 = 0$
10	0.94	$10 \times 0.94 = 9.4$
20	0.80	$20 \times 0.80 = 16$
30	0.52	$30 \times 0.52 = 15.2$
40	0.17	$40 \times 0.17 = 6.8$
50	0.03	$50 \times 0.03 = 1.5$

of profit on the contract. He then proposed that this could measured by multiplying the expected profit by the probability of winning to give an expected percentage profit, as shown in Table 13.7. This indicates that, in this case, statistically the maximum expected profit would be 16%, obtained with a mark-up of 20%.

It is of course extremely unlikely that contractors will always be competing against the same one competitor for every project, but the same principles can be used to assess the chances of winning against each of a number of competitors. The probability of winning against a range of contractors is the product of the chances of beating them each individually, as shown in Table 13.8, and the maximum expected profit can again be calculated.

The model set out in Table 13.8 assumes that it is possible to collect information about the price submitted for each contract by each competitor. This may be an unreasonable assumption, since:

1. Clients would not normally make this information available.

Table 13.8 Expected value of profits (several competitors)

Mark-up %	Probability of beating			Expected profit %
	A	B	C	
−10	1.00	1.00	1.00	$-10 \times 1.00 \times 1.00 \times 1.00 = -10$
0	0.99	0.97	0.96	$0 \times 0.99 \times 0.97 \times 0.96 = 0$
10	0.94	0.95	0.93	$10 \times 0.94 \times 0.95 \times 0.93 = 8.48$
20	0.80	0.75	0.70	$20 \times 0.80 \times 0.75 \times 0.85 = 8.40$
30	0.52	0.60	0.55	$30 \times 0.52 \times 0.60 \times 0.55 = 5.14$
40	0.17	0.14	0.13	$40 \times 0.17 \times 0.14 \times 0.13 = 0.12$
50	0.03	0.07	0.10	$50 \times 0.03 \times 0.07 \times 0.10 = 0.01$

2. The technique assumes that the firm has information about a sufficient number of tenders against the same competitors to allow meaningful probability distributions to be developed. Hillebrandt (1974) estimates that 50 bids would be required for each competitor to give a reasonable level of reliability.

It is, however, common practice for clients to make available a list of tender sums, but without naming the contractors concerned. Woodward (1975) therefore suggested that the problem can be overcome by treating all competitors as one 'average contractor'. In this case, only one frequency distribution is required for the bids as a whole, and the overall probability of submitting the lowest tender is therefore the probability of beating the average contractor raised to the power n where n is the number of contractors submitting tenders; i.e. in the original case the probability of beating all competitors was $P_1 \times P_2 \times P_3 \times \ldots \times P_n$, whereas in this case it is $P_{average}^n$. The method is illustrated in Table 13.9.

The assumption that each competitor can be treated as an 'average' contractor is open to question, but Woodward further suggests that there may be little to be gained in terms of greater accuracy of prediction from collecting data on each individual competitor unless there is reason to believe that one of the tendering contractors will behave differently from the norm. Note also that the data involved represents the market performance of competitor firms, the behaviour of each of whom is governed by their own commercial pressures. Their behaviour can therefore be expected to change over time as their own trading environment changes. The information must therefore be current (i.e. it must be collected and updated at regular intervals). Hillebrandt (1974) estimates that the data used should span a period of no more than about three months.

Table 13.9 Expected value of profits (four 'average' competitors)

Mark-up (%)	Probability of beating 'average' competitor	Expected profit (%)
−10	1.00	$-10 \times 1.00^4 = -10$
0	0.99	$0 \times 0.99^4 = 0$
10	0.94	$10 \times 0.94^4 = 7.81$
20	0.80	$20 \times 0.80^4 = 8.19$
30	0.52	$30 \times 0.52^4 = 2.19$
40	0.17	$40 \times 0.17^4 = 0.033$
50	0.03	$50 \times 0.03^4 = 0.00004$

Table 13.10 Mark-up needed to win (after Woodward, 1975)

Winning bid (£)	Our cost (£)	Ratio col.1:col.2	Mark-up needed to win (%)	Rank order
12 040 000	12 100 000	0.9950	−0.50	8
6 320 000	6 200 000	1.0193	1.93	5
9 740 000	9 200 000	1.0586	5.86	2
19 200 000	20 000 000	0.9600	−4.00	10
4 900 000	5 020 000	0.9760	−2.40	9
7 300 000	7 040 000	1.0369	3.69	4
4 020 000	3 650 000	1.1013	10.13	1
15 600 000	15 570 000	1.0019	0.19	7
10 230 000	9 820 000	1.0417	4.17	3
8 980 000	8 840 000	1.0158	1.58	6

Note that the mark-up needed to win (col. 4) is calculated from (col.3 −1.00) × 100

Friedman's basic model, as briefly described, depends upon knowledge of both winning and losing bids, but it is possible that details of the losing bids will not always be available. It is, however, highly likely that the winning bid figure will generally be known, and it has been argued that this figure is, after all, the most important, since a contractor would only be interested in knowing how its bid performed against the winning bid. Several researchers have attempted to develop models on this basis, based largely on the work of Gates (1967). Gates suggested that by comparing its own bid to the winning bid a contractor could calculate the mark-up which would have been needed in order to win the contract. Table 13.10, giving details for 10 hypothetical contracts, gives the general idea, and is adapted from Woodward (1975).

From Table 13.10 it can be seen that with a mark-up in excess of 10% the contractor would only have won one of the contracts listed. It would have won two with a mark-up of 5.86%, three with a mark-up of 4.17% and would have won all of the contracts with a mark-up of −4%. Note that by also including the second lowest price for those projects which it actually won, the contractor can check on the competitiveness of the level of its own mark-up.

A number of writers (e.g. Gates (1967), Broemser (1968), Benjamin (1969), Park (1979)) have proposed ways to increase the accuracy of the probability type model by developing variations and refinements to take account of additional factors such as project size, complexity and duration. Beeston (1983) describes a similar method based on the use of a cumulative frequency distribution, including a method of adjustment to allow estimators to make allowances for the number of tenderers competing for any one project, for short-term variations in market price trends and for the perceived general desirability of the project. He also includes a detailed example calculation of his method together with advice on testing and tuning for optimum performance. Griffis (1992) extends the general theory by developing a more sophisticated multi-dimensional model of competitors' potential bidding behaviour, and also reports that a Canadian company, Anaheim Technologies, has developed a commercial expert system to evaluate a 'best' mark-up. Park and Chapin (1992) develop the theory by constructing a series of models reflecting the situation given differing numbers of bidders and different sizes and types of project. They go on to develop a computer package called Databid which they assert is not a theory but a proven method by which contractors can improve their tendering success rates.

Friedman's model and its subsequent derivatives attempt to assist the contractor to find the lowest bid in a tender auction. Ioannou and Leu (1993), however, point out that some countries use other methods of choosing the successful tender, generally by choosing a bid which bears some predefined relationship to either the mean or the median of all bids submitted. Ioannou and Leu go on to develop a competitive bidding model for use with the average bid method of contractor selection.

Teo and Scott (1994) extend Freidman's model in a study based on a sample of 135 renovation contracts placed in the UK between 1984 and 1987, and go on to develop a model designed to calculate the 'best' bid price for this type of work given the contractor's net cost estimate.

13.8   ECONOMETRIC MODELS

Hillebrandt (1974) points out that the use of probability-based models could have significant shortcomings when applied to construction. The basic problem as she saw it was that many of the variable factors involved are uncertainties to which no probabilities can be assigned, and that therefore the use of probability techniques can result in the use of simplifying assumptions which reduce the technique's reliability. She therefore approached the problem from the point of view of helping the decision-maker to decide whether it is worthwhile submitting a bid including some predetermined mark-up level. She proposed supplementing the existing probability-based techniques with an iterative technique incorporating subjective expert judgements within an econometric framework called Shackle's Degree of Potential Surprise. In essence, the approach derives a series of values combining the decision-maker's degree of potential satisfaction in winning the project at varying levels of mark-up with his or her personal risk preference.

This technique is interesting because it attempts to incorporate the personal feelings and the expert knowledge of the bidders in the formal decision-making process. The technique as presented by Hillebrandt is somewhat involved, and it is unlikely that many contractors would have the necessary skills to use it, but it does have some merit. Unfortunately, few researchers have taken up the approach, but work by Benjamin (1969), Fellows and Langford (1980) and Ibbs and Crandall (1982) has developed some facets of the approach.

It would seem at least possible that bidding performance could be improved by the formal incorporation of potentially unstructured 'expert' knowledge in the decision-making process. There may be some worth in exploring Hillebrandt's approach again, perhaps using some kind of fuzzy logic approach.

13.9 REGRESSION MODELS

Other researchers (e.g. Skitmore and Patchell, 1990) have suggested that the use of regression techniques might assist in modelling the bidding process. The basic form of the regression model equation as given by Skitmore and Patchell is:

$$Y = a + b_1X_1 + b_2X_2 + b_3X_3 + \ldots + b_nX_n$$

where Y is the observation we wish to predict (e.g. the lowest bid price), a is some constant, X_1, X_2 etc. are characteristics which we believe will influence the prediction, and b_1, b_2 etc. represent the weightings associated with the various characteristics. Thus, in a bidding model, Y would be the value of the lowest bid, X_1 might be 'our' estimated cost, X_2 might be a measure of project size, X_3 might be the number of bidders etc. Details of the various regression techniques are well described in Skitmore and Patchell (1990), but since there are so many uncertainties (and a limited theoretical research base) involving identification of the factors which might be important in making the winning bid, the basic approach, as stated by Skitmore and Patchell, boils down to:

...simply an empirical search for the set of quantifiable items which produces the most reliable estimates for Y.

This then implies a sizeable database incorporating all possible items that might affect the cost if the model is to be reliable. Since the various factors are not yet known, compilation of the relevant database is likely to be difficult. Skitmore and Patchell, however, give an example analysis of an attempt to derive a model for office blocks in a variety of locations in the UK.

While this technique may hold some promise for the future, it appears that it is a long way from providing a working tool. Skitmore and Patchell admit that:

...research in regression is far from comprehensive and, because of the arbitrary means employed, has not been reported well enough to allow any incremental progress to be made. Also, with the confusion over reliability measures, it has not been possible to properly evaluate the progress that has been made.

There would again seem to be plenty of scope for further research in this area.

13.10   CONCLUSIONS

Bidding models have been around for almost 40 years, and we should question why they have not become more widely used in the construction industry.

Firstly, it is essential to recognise the deficiencies which result from using statistically based techniques on their own to forecast the outcome of any particular specific event, e.g. the award of any single tender. These techniques do not attempt to predict the outcome of any particular tender: they simply attempt to predict a trend over a period of time, and it may be that construction companies do not submit enough tenders in any given period of time for the trend to become established or useful. In addition, the various techniques described all rely on simplifying assumptions of one kind or another, and it must be recognised that this will almost certainly affect the reliability of the results. Nonetheless, there appears to be some evidence that, used with care, bidding models can give contractors a competitive advantage. Hillebrandt (1974), for example, says:

> It seems clear and acceptable that the determination of the probability of getting a job using past data is a very valuable piece of information for a firm to have.... Moreover, the contribution of this approach is useful in its own right because it has been shown to yield better results in tendering than those which would have obtained by purely 'hunch' methods.

There would also seem to be some support for this view from more recent writers, e.g. Skitmore (1989, p. 184), who says:

> The likelihood of project acquisition would seem... to be a strong candidate for modelling in a statistical manner the terms of the probability of entering the lowest bid for the project.

Rutter (1993) perhaps sums up the situation when he suggests that such models can offer a framework, a tool, which when used in conjunction with other signals can help decision-makers to improve their tendering decisions. Notwithstanding the apparent advantages, however, there is little evidence that bidding models are widely used at present either in the UK or in the USA. Some of the reasons may be:

1. That the number of projects bid in any particular period may be too small to allow the collection of sufficient information for the construction of a meaningful probability distribution.

2. That contractors may be unable (or unwilling) to commit themselves to collecting the necessary database of information.

3. That contractors may not know what techniques are available and/or may not understand how to use them. They may simply be happier simply to trust to 'hunches'.

13.11   REFERENCES

Ahmad I. and Minkarah I. (1988) 'Questionnaire survey on bidding in construction', *Journal of Management in Engineering*, July 1988, pp. 229–43.

Al-Tabtabai H. and Diekman J.E. (1992) 'Judgemental forecasting in construction projects', *Construction Management and Economics*, Vol. 10, pp. 19–30.

Ansoff H.I. (1965) *Corporate Strategy*, Penguin, London.

Beeston D.T. (1983) *Statistical Methods for Building Price Data*, E. & F.N. Spon, London.

Benjamin N.B.H. (1969) Competitive bidding for construction contracts, *PhD Dissertation*, Stanford University.

Broemser G.M. (1968) Competitive bidding in the construction industry, *PhD Dissertation*, Stanford University.

CIOB (1983) *Code of Estimating Practice*, Chartered Institute of Building, London.

Eastham R.A. (1987) The use of content analysis to determine a weighted model of the contractor's tendering process', in *Building Cost Modelling and Computers* (ed. Brandon P.S.), E. & F.N. Spon, London.

Fellows R and Langford D. (1980) 'Decision theory and tendering', *Building Technology and Management*, October 1980, pp. 36–9.

Friedman L. (1956) 'A competitive bidding strategy' *Operations Research*, Vol. IV, pp. 104–12.

Gates M. (1967) 'Bidding strategies and probabilities' *Journal of the Construction Division, American Society of Civil Engineers*, Vol. 97 (CO2), pp. 277–303.

Griffis F. (1992) 'Bidding strategy: winning over key competitors' *Journal of Construction Engineering and Management*, March, pp. .

Hillebrandt P.M. (1974) *Economic Theory and the Construction Industry*, Macmillan, London.

Ioannou P.G. (1988) 'Bidding models – symmetry and state of information', *Journal of Construction Engineering and Management*, Vol. 115, No. 2, pp. 237–57.

Ioannou P.G. and Leu S.S. (1993) 'Average-bid method – competitive bidding strategy', *Journal of Construction Engineering and Management*, Vol. 199, No. 1.

Kangari R. and Riggs L.S. (1988) 'Portfolio management in construction', *Construction Management and Economics*, Vol. 6, pp. 161–9.

Moselhi O., Hegazy T. and Fazio P. (1993) 'DBID: Analogy based DSS for bidding in construction', *Journal of Construction Engineering and Management*, Vol. 119, No. 3, p. 466.

Odusote A. and Fellows R. (1992) 'An examination of the importance of resource considerations when contractors make project selection decisions', *Construction Management and Economics*, March 1992, pp. 137–51.

Park W.R. (1979) *Construction Bidding for Profit*, John Wiley, New York.

Park W.R. and Chapin W.B. (1992) *Construction Bidding: Strategic Pricing for Profit*, 2nd edn, John Wiley, New York.

Rutter G. (1993) *Construction Economics: Is there such a thing?*, Construction Papers No. 18 1993, Chartered Institute of Building, London.

Shash M. (1993) 'Factors considered in tendering decisions by top UK contractors' *Construction Management and Economics*, March 1993, pp. 111–18.

Skitmore M. (1989) *Contract Bidding in Construction*, Longman Scientific and Technical, London.

Skitmore M. and Patchell B. (1990) 'Contract price forecasting and bidding techniques', in *Quantity Surveying Techniques: New Directions* (ed. Brandon P.S.), BSP Professional Books, London.

Teo D.H.P., Quah L.K., Torrance V.B. and Okoro M.I. (1991) Risk evaluation and decision support system for tendering and refurbishment contracts, in *Management, Quality and Economics in Building* (eds. Bezalga A. and Brandon P.S.), E. & F.N. Spon, London.

Teo H.P. and Scott W.F. (1994) 'Bidding model for refurbishment work', *Journal of Construction Engineering and Management*, Vol. 120, No. 2, pp. 257–73.

Woodward J.F. (1975) *Quantitative Methods in Construction Management and Design*, Macmillan, London.

14   The Competitive Tendering Process – A Client's View

14.1   INTRODUCTION

Competitive tendering, particularly for public works, has a long history in the UK. The origins of the practice are reported by Powell (1980, p. 28) to stem from the early 19th century, and basically arose out of dissatisfaction with the existing systems of measure and value, where tradesmen were paid directly by the client for work as it proceeded. Powell, quoting Elsam (1826), writes that:

> Measurement of completed building work prior to payment caused enormous difficulties and frequent disputes, with the '...distressful, often the ruinous uncertainty of common estimates...' by measurers who were said to be '...seldom if ever right in their conjectures'. The response of Commissioners reporting on the Public Office of Works in 1812–1813 was to favour competitive tendering as a superior alternative to measure and value.

This chapter considers aspects of the tendering process from the point of view of the construction client. It examines the client's objectives, and attempts to indicate the factors that are important in satisfying them in the context of a variety of procurement methodologies.

14.2   THE CLIENT'S OBJECTIVES

A client embarking on construction work is interested first and foremost in the finished product. The client is not usually concerned about how the finished result is achieved, and indeed may know little or nothing either about the construction process or even about the structure of the construction industry. The client will therefore usually appoint a team of professional advisors to help it realise its aims and to safeguard its interests. It will usually also be part of the professional advisors' role to help the client to decide the best way to satisfy its needs.

The professional advisors will help the client to clarify just what its needs are in functional terms, and they will then be expected to define those needs in terms of time, of quality, and sometimes of quantity of the finished product in order that contractors can submit prices for the work.

It has already been shown that most construction works are to a greater or lesser extent unique, i.e. every project is to some extent different and poses its own problems. This then means that not only the technical problems but also the time and cost factors will require detailed assessment on a job-by-job basis. The construction market-place is therefore unlike any other, and the problems involved from the client's point of view in buying construction work are also unique. Buying construction work is not like buying a car or even an aeroplane, where one can start from the manufacturer's published price and negotiate discounts of various kinds. With the possible exception of speculative development, there is no generally available published list of prices for construction work. Each contract tends to be a separate standalone bargain made between the client and the contractor, the precise terms of which are governed by the complexities of the particular project, the commercial state of the tendering firms and by the market conditions at the time the tenders are invited.

Since this is so, and since the client is, of course, aware that the successful contractor would ideally like to make as much profit as possible from the deal, clients will naturally try to strike the best bargain they can for the work, and this will normally involve some kind of competition.

14.3   TENDERING PRACTICE

Having said all of this it might appear that it would be in the client's best interest to seek the lowest possible price for the work, and the easiest way to do this would obviously be to prepare some tender documentation and to allow anyone who wishes to do so to submit a tender. This form of tendering is called 'open tendering', and is usually done by advertising the project in the trade press. This process will obviously maximise the competition, and it is likely that it will result in the lowest available price for the job.

From a public sector point of view, it is argued by some that this method provides for the maximum degree of public accountability in that the lowest price is seen to be obtained in an open and fair competition. But what is really required in the public sector is surely not simply to obtain the lowest price but to obtain the best value for the money spent, and there is considerable doubt about whether this can be achieved by taking the lowest price in a largely unrestricted open competition, where the number of bids submitted is likely to be both unpredictable and probably excessive. Drew (1993) points out that:

> a sample of Hong Kong Government open tender contracts contained an average of 17 bidders competing for each contract, with a range of between 2 and 35 bidders.

Given this situation it is likely that the lowest tender price will be less than the true market value for the work, and therefore that the successful contractor will subsequently seek to increase its ultimate price through the submission of claims. Open tendering does have significant disadvantages from both the client's and the tendering contractors' points of view, but despite the fact that the practice has been roundly condemned in the UK at regular intervals for almost the last 50 years (see for example Simon (1944), who recommended that it should be replaced by selective tendering), the method is still used.

From the tendering contractors' point of view the problem is that the higher the number of tenderers the lower the probability of any one contractor winning the project (if there are only, say, three tenderers then, all things being equal, each contractor has a 1 in 3 chance of winning purely by random chance, whereas if there are 50 contractors tendering an individual contractor's chances of winning are only 1 in 50). Also, with open tendering of this sort there is a strong likelihood that the firm submitting the lowest price will be the one that has made the biggest mistake(s) in its calculations. Reputable contractors will therefore not be prepared to put in a lot of effort if the odds of winning the job are small, and may even consider it not worth their while to submit a price at all, thus leaving the field open for perhaps less reputable contractors.

On the other hand, the major problem from the client's point of view is that although it may get a very cheap price it is likely that it may know little or nothing about the skills, capabilities and financial soundness of the lowest tenderer. If it chooses the lowest tender submitted in this way it therefore runs an increased risk of entering into a contract with a contractor who may fail to complete the work within the required time, cost and quality parameters.

We can therefore see that it is not always in the client's interest to seek the cheapest possible price for the work. We have already seen that it is part of the professional advisors' role to help the client to clarify its ideas about what it actually wants in terms of building function, quality, potential time span and budget long before the project gets to the tender stage. In order for the project to get to the stage of selecting a contractor the client must have already made up its mind about its time requirements and its outline budget. What the client should be looking for at tender stage therefore is a reasonable degree of compliance with the time and cost guidelines already established with the help of its professional team. Note particularly that when the quantity surveyor prepares the early stage estimates and cost plans this is not, generally speaking, an attempt to forecast what the lowest price will be. Instead, the quantity surveyor's estimates, upon which the budget will be based, will normally have been prepared on the basis of the perception of a fair price for the work, bearing in mind prevailing market conditions. Essentially, what most clients want at tender stage is to avoid shocks, but it is of course recognised that some clients, particularly those with little knowledge of the industry, still consider it important to obtain the lowest possible price for the job. It is part of the professional team's job to advise the client about the pitfalls set out above.

The client's objectives from the tendering process can then be summarised as follows:

1. To obtain a fair price for the work, bearing in mind the general state of the construction market at the time.

2. To enter into an agreement with a contractor who possesses the necessary technical skill, resources and financial backing to give the client the best possible chance that the works will be completed within the required time, cost and quality standards.

Drew (1993) contends that:

for every contract there is the optimum bidder who is not only capable of fulfilling the client's requirements in terms of time, quality and risk but also in respect of cost is also willing and able to submit a bid lower than any competitor. A fundamental goal of any competitive bidding system is to reveal the identity of this optimum bidder and determine the bid price.

Achievement of these objectives will involve:

1. Selection of an appropriate procurement methodology.

2. The preparation of appropriate tender documentation.

3. Identification and selection of an appropriate number of suitable contractors who are willing to tender for the work.

4. Choice and acceptance of the most suitable tender.

The detailed consideration of the factors inherent in the selection of an appropriate procurement methodology and the preparation of appropriate tender documentation are outside the scope of this text. It is, however, important to remember that the documentation should be adequate to allow the tenderers to submit realistic tender prices. For the client to be able to choose the most acceptable tender it is essential that all tenders are prepared on a common basis. In other words, it is in the client's interest as much as the contractors' for the tender documentation to be unambiguous and as complete as possible.

The National Joint Consultative Committee for Building publishes Codes of Procedure for single-stage selective tendering, two-stage selective tendering and tendering for design and build projects to provide sound guidelines and encourage good practice.

14.4   IDENTIFICATION AND SELECTION OF SUITABLE CONTRACTORS

It has already been established that one of the client's objectives, perhaps the prime objective, in entering into the tender process is to enter into an agreement with a contractor who possesses the necessary technical skill, resources and financial backing to give the client the best possible chance that the works will be completed within the required time and quality standards at a price which is competitive but fair, bearing in mind the state of the construction market at the time. Since it has already been established that open tendering is not generally considered to be a good idea, it will then be obvious that the aim should be to ensure that *all* of the firms invited to submit tenders should have the necessary skills and resources to complete the project successfully. This then implies some kind of pre-selection process before tenders are actually invited. This process is sometimes called prequalification. Two main questions arise:

1. How many contractors should be invited to submit tenders?

2. How should the contractors be selected?

14.5   HOW MANY CONTRACTORS?

When deciding how many contractors to invite to tender we must bear in mind the competing demands of the client and the tendering contractors. On the one hand, the tendering contractors may only be interested in submitting a bid if there is a reasonable chance of winning (i.e. from their point of view the number of tenderers needs to be as small as possible), but on the other hand there may be pressure from individual contractors to be included on tender lists, particularly when work is tight. The client, however, will want to see a sufficiently large number of tenders to be reassured that it really is getting the best deal available in the market-place at the time.

ᵗh the 1989 edition of the Code of Procedure for Single Stage
ring, and the 1983 edition of the Code of Procedure for Two
published by the National Joint Consultative Committee for
....ʁ recommend that the number of tenders to be invited for projects let
using the 'traditional' procurement approach should not exceed six, regardless
of the size of the contract. Most government and quasi-governmental bodies
will have their own rules.

Large projects let using variants of the design and build technique pose
special problems for tendering contractors because of the very high levels of
speculative expenditure required to prepare a bid. The issue is graphically
illustrated by Potts and Sanvido (1994):

> Recently, the US Army Corps of Engineers awarded a contract for the
> US$58.4 million, 55,720 m^2, Sparkman Center for Missile Excellence in
> Huntsville, Alabama.... Sixteen teams bid on the project. The fifteen
> losing bidders contend that they could not afford to repeat the process...
> the Corps did consider short-listing firms, but decided that this would
> lead to a protest because of the qualification of the teams. The Corps
> felt that it would be in the best interest of the teams to review all
> proposals.

Experience in the UK seems to show that in a normal commercial environment contractors may decline to tender for this type of work where the
number of tenderers exceeds three or four.

For civil engineering projects the ICE recommends a minimum of four and
a maximum of eight bids, with numbers invited tending towards the lower
end of the range for larger projects. There is some evidence (Flanagan and
Norman, 1989) that four or five bidders will ensure a genuinely competitive
bid.

14.6   PREQUALIFICATION

The prequalification process basically consists of evaluating the available pool
of potential tenderers, identified either by advertisement or invitation, against
some given set of criteria in order to find some group of firms who are all
considered competent to carry out the work and who are expected to provide
an acceptable range of prices. A number of techniques are commonly used.

An obvious first step is to determine what the required criteria for prequalification are to be. At the very simplest level the basic criterion is that the firms
should all be at least competent to undertake the work. In many cases, and
particularly in the case of small contracts or very specialised work, a number
of contractors might be chosen simply on the basis of work that they have
done before for the same architect or engineer. In this case the prequalification

process is almost completely personal and subjective, and may simply involve sending a letter to each firm giving basic details about the job and asking if the firm is willing to submit a tender. As we have already seen, however, except in the most unusual circumstances, most firms will tend to accept invitations of this kind even if they have no intention of submitting a *bona fide* tender. This method therefore has deficiencies and should not be used on its own except for very small projects. Drew and Skitmore (1992) are particularly scathing:

> [Prequalification] is often accomplished by crude subjective assessment of bidders' capabilities based on the prequalifier's first- or second-hand knowledge of the bidders.... Such a procedure is naturally rather unreliable and may result in the selection of bidders that are either not interested or not able to provide competitive bids for a contract. There is also the possibility that other ready, willing and able potential bidders may be neglected.

It is therefore apparent that considerable care needs to be taken if prequalification exercises are to be successful, and a more sophisticated technique is generally considered desirable on larger projects. Some possibilities are as follows.

14.7   FINANCIAL MODELS

The construction industry is well known for the high incidence of business failures amongst its constituent firms. Young (1991) reports that in the years between 1973 and 1983 construction-related firms:

> ...represent 35% of limited companies failing over that period.... The manufacturing sector was second to construction with significantly less reported failures; only 10% in all. The overwhelming evidence suggests that the construction industry was the most vulnerable sector during that 10 year period and that the same is true in the early 1990s, given current business collapses.

Confirmation that this is not just a British problem comes from Kangari *et al.* (1992), who report that in the USA 'The failure rate among construction companies has reached a critically high level', and Lenard (1991) points out that there seems to be little or no relationship between financial failure and a contractor's technical capability.

It is therefore important that, in addition to assessing firms' technical and managerial skills, an assessment is also made of their financial standing and resources. Many financial modelling techniques exist, and they are widely used by major organisations, including most government and quasi-government bodies, both to evaluate contractors for specific large projects and also in the compilation of approved tender lists. Russell and Jaselskis (1993) report that:

> Numerous studies have been conducted related to predictive business failure models. A majority of these studies used discriminant analysis and variables principally involving financial ratios to predict the bankruptcy of a business.

The simplest and crudest model simply compares a contractor's current assets with current liabilities, as is now shown:

$$MFC = (CA - CL)C$$

where:

MFC = an index indicating maximum financial capability

CA = contractor's current assets

CL = contractor's current liabilities

C = some multiplying coefficient to reduce the numbers to manageable proportions

This model has the advantage of simplicity, but it goes no further than simply analysing one aspect of financial performance. It has, however, already been shown that the evaluation also needs to include an assessment of other operational factors as well. Some users of the simple single ratio model have included a further term to take account of this, and the earlier model then becomes:

$$MFC = [(CA - CL)C]M$$

where M is some coefficient (perhaps on a scale of 1–10) representing the decision-maker's subjective judgement of the contractor's past record in terms of safety, past performance, attitude etc.

Although single index models of this type are commonly used they are very crude, and Russell (1992) states that in the USA they have been found to be inaccurate in determining contractors' capacity and performance capabilities.

Research by Kangari *et al.* (1992) in the USA, using regression analysis based on a large sample of construction data, found that the financial ratios shown in Table 14.1 appeared to be important in examining a company's financial strength, and these seem to correlate reasonably well with those identified in a study of the general literature by Langford *et al.* (1993).

Table 14.1 Important financial ratios (Kangari et al., 1992)

1. Current assets to current liabilities
2. Total liabilities to net worth
3. Total assets to revenues
4. Revenues to net working capital
5. Return on total assets
6. Return on net worth

Kangari *et al.* go on to develop a regression model incorporating all six ratios to give an index for overall financial performance, together with a set of tables giving regression coefficients for a variety of types of construction company, normalisation coefficients for each of the ratios, and size factors for each ratio based on the company's asset value. They do, however, make the point that an index of financial performance is no good on its own: it needs to be compared with the overall performance of the industry as a whole in order to give a true picture. They therefore calculate the required probability distributions and go on to give step by step instructions for the use of their model in practice. The Kangari model represents a considerable step forward from the simple single ratio analysis, but is presumably not directly applicable outside the USA without recalculation of all of the appropriate tables.

The Z-model approach (Altman, 1968, 1973), which has been widely used in general business for many years in the USA to identify potential company insolvencies, is based on the analysis of selected financial ratios using a technique called multivariate discriminant analysis to generate a single score, called the Z-score, intended to give a summative measure of the company's general financial position. Langford *et al.* (1993) applied both ratio analysis and the Z-score model to three recently failed construction firms. They report that both techniques predicted failure in two out of the three cases, but the sample size is much too small to make any wide-ranging predictions.

14.8 INTEGRATED MODELS

Financial models of the type shown above only represent the contractor's financial position, and there have been a number of attempts to develop alternative models to derive some overall index of potential contractor performance taking into account all of the factors which the client and its advisors consider to be important for a particular specific project. While some of the factors might be specific to particular projects (e.g. a particular technical skill), some of the factors which might typically be included in any integrated analysis might, in addition to financial performance, include things like:

Management ability

Past performance in terms of time and cost overruns

Safety rating

Quality assessment

Claims policy

Some researchers (e.g. Drew and Skitmore, 1992) also advocate including an assessment of the contractor's past bidding policy as part of the model, arguing that contractors with little experience of the particular type of project in question are more likely, either by accident or miscalculation, to submit unrealistic or suicidally low bids for the work.

While all of these factors, and perhaps others, may certainly be important, the weighting attached to each will need to be carefully considered for each project, and it would appear that this is where the real professional skill lies.

The simplest models take a basic linear form, such as:

$$AR_j = \sum_{i=1}^{n} (W_i)(R_{ij})$$

where

AR_j = aggregate rating or performance index of contractor j

n = total number of decision criteria in the model

W_i = weighting given to decision criterion i (sum $W_i = 1$ for $i = 1\ldots n$)

R_{ij} = rating given to contractor j for criterion i

This type of model is quite widely used, and a description of a computerised algorithm for contractor preselection using this technique, called QUALIFIER-1, is given in Russell and Skibniewski (1990).

The major problem with this type of model is that it only allows for one subjective value to be input to each of the criteria, that is it only provides a snapshot view of a contractor's performance at a particular moment in time. This would be acceptable if the contractor concerned had only completed one project, but this is not usually the case, and a combined view of the contractor's performance over a range of work would normally be required. The position is further complicated by the fact that a contractor's performance might not be consistent from one project to another: for example, management expertise on one project which goes well might be rated as very good, whereas on another project which does not go so well the same criterion might be rated as only average. What is really required is some means of incorporating values for ratings in the form of probability assessments rather than as single deterministic figures. Another problem is that such assessments are subjective. This type of model is essentially static; it is processed once to achieve the contractor's rating and cannot readily be updated as more information about the contractor becomes available.

These objections can be overcome by models of the form:

$$AR_j = \sum_{i=1}^{n} (W_i)(EAR_{ij})$$

where

AR_j = contractor's performance index for contractor j

n = number of criteria to be included in the model

W_i = weighting given to criterion i

EAR_{ji} = total Earned Aggregate Rating for contractor j for criterion i

The Earned Aggregate Rating (EAR) is given by generating a probability distribution from the various observations for each criterion, the totals being summed as follows:

$$EAR_{ji} = \sum_{k=1}^{n} (P_i)(R_{jik})$$

where

n = total number of ratings used for each criterion

P_i = probability of occurrence of criterion i assigned by the decision-maker (summation of $P_i = 1$ for $i=1...n$)

R_{jik} = rating k for criterion i for contractor j

Russell (1992) gives an example of the use of such a formula, together with other variations of multi-attribute linear models, and Potter and Sanvido (1994) develop a complex methodology for prequalification of design and build teams in which each team is assessed separately against three separate sets of criteria: (1) project specific, (2) business and (3) technical team skills. Again the choice of specific criteria is context-specific.

14.9   MODELS USING ADVANCED MATHEMATICAL TECHNIQUES

Other researchers have developed more sophisticated models. In particular, Diekman (1981) has developed a model using utility theory and Nguyen (1985) has developed a model using fuzzy sets. Both of these approaches are summarised in Russell (1992), but it appears that none has achieved widespread practical usage.

Tam (1993) applies multivariate discriminant analysis to derive a general model for likely contractor performance within a specific locality, in his case Hong Kong. The result is expressed as a Z-score, as described earlier. After having examined 20 different variables, Tam constructs a discriminant function model incorporating the following predictor variables:

Project complexity

Percentage of professionally qualified staff employed by the contractor

Project leader's experience

Contractor's past performance

Origin of the company (local Hong Kong Chinese or foreign)

Degree of control by architect or engineer

Russell and Jaselskis (1993) derive a similar function using American data to predict the likelihood of contractor failure on specific projects. Note that in this case 'failure' is not purely defined as financial failure, but is instead:

deemed as a significant breach of the contractor's legal responsibilities to the owner, for example bankruptcy or material breach of contract relating to meeting desired project objectives such as cost, schedule, safety and quality.

Following a detailed analysis of 42 projects, Russell and Jaselskis found that only four key inputs were significant in predicting the probability of failure as defined above. These are (1) owner–contractor evaluation effort, (2) cost monitoring effort by the owner, (3) the level of support received by the project manager from the contractor's senior management through the course of the project and (4) the early involvement of the project manager measured as a percentage of the project duration.

It would appear, from the lack of correlation between the predictor values obtained by Tam and those derived by Russell and Jaselskis, that such models are locally dependent, in other words the same factors may not be significant in different locations. This is evidently another potentially fertile area for construction economics research.

14.10   CURRENT DEVELOPMENTS

It will be seen that the prequalification problem is still not completely solved, and research is ongoing on several fronts.

It has been suggested (Russell *et al.*, 1990) that computer-based 'expert system' technology could be used to model the prequalification process. This approach would seem to have promise if a suitable database of rules could be established. It should certainly be relatively easy to develop a set of rules to mimic the human process of checking a contractor's financial stability, but the modelling of subjective criteria such as quality of work or quality of technical expertise would appear to be rather more difficult.

This area is at the very forefront of research, and an experimental expert system called QUALIFIER-2 is described in Russell *et al.* (1990).

It has also been suggested by researchers that none of the existing types of model uses all of the available data about contractors to the full. Nonetheless, each of the existing types of model has its advantages for specific parts of the process. It has therefore been suggested that the real way forward would be to integrate all of the existing models into a computer-based hybrid decision support system incorporating the best parts of each of the existing models. A system of this type is outlined in Russell (1992).

14.11   CHOOSING THE BEST BUY

At first glance, choosing the best buy might seem to be absurdly simple. If all of the contractors on the tender list have been carefully chosen then surely should not the winning tender simply be the lowest bid? It will in any event be difficult to persuade the client otherwise.

In many cases, particularly when the dates for commencement and completion are given in the tender documents, this will of course normally be the case, but there is still the possibility of contractors either accidentally or deliberately submitting unrealistically low bids. Some researchers argue that we can at least partially overcome this problem by making the contractor's past bidding pattern part of the prequalification model, but this will not overcome the problem altogether, and it will also tend to operate against new firms or those attempting to move to new sectors of the market. Remember also that clients at tender stage generally want simply to avoid shocks; they normally will not have got to that stage at all unless they are happy with the order of cost projected by their professional advisors, so provided the professional cost advisor has done its job properly, unrealistically low tenders should generally be apparent by comparison with the pre-tender estimates. In the case of error of course, the lowest tenderer has the option to withdraw before the tender is accepted, but this still leaves the contractor who submits a low bid to get the work, with a plan to recover additional monies from claims during the course of the project. This of course is a situation that the client should be anxious to avoid, since accepting the lowest tender in these circumstances may involve it in much higher out-turn costs.

In an attempt to prevent contractors from 'buying' work in this way, some countries are reported to have tried alternative methods of awarding contracts with a view to accepting a fair price for the work rather than the lowest tender.

At the very simplest level this may simply involve automatically disqualifying the lowest tenderer as a matter of course. This would certainly put an end to contractors submitting tenders which simply try to find the lowest possible bid price, but it is somewhat crude and in any case does not deal with the situation where more than one contractor is attempting to 'buy' the work.

Ioannou and Leu (1993) report that variants of what has become known as the 'average bid' method have been tried in Italy and in Taiwan, and Herbsman and Ellis (1992) report that a similar method has been tried in Peru. In all cases the methods involve accepting the tender which most closely satisfies some predefined relationship with the average of the bids submitted and/or the predicted cost. Different methods approach the problem in different ways, and the major difference is in the way the average is calculated. Some methods, for example, simply calculate the arithmetic average of the bids, while others will exclude all extreme outlying bids and calculate the average of the remainder. Similarly, in some systems the winning tenderer is the one whose bid falls closest to the average (e.g. Taiwan), whereas in other systems (e.g. Italy) the winner is the tenderer whose bid is closest to but less than the average. The rules governing the Peruvian Government system, as explained by Herbsman and Ellis, are shown in Table 14.2.

Some examples showing various options are shown in Table 14.3.

The use of an 'average bid' method of tendering can greatly lessen the chances of the client accepting an unrealistically low bid for the work, but at the risk of excluding what might be a *bona fide* lowest tender.

Table 14.2 Peruvian Government bidding system (Herbsman and Ellis, 1992)

1. The average of all bids and the base budget is calculated
2. All bids which lie 10% or more above and below this average are eliminated
3. The average of the remaining bids and the base budget is calculated
4. The contract is awarded to the bid immediately below the second average or, should none of the bids lie below the second average to the bid which most closely approximates to the average.

Table 14.3 'Average bid' methods: some hypothetical examples

Tender list	Bid (£m)
Contractor 1	8.85
Contractor 2	9.00
Contractor 3	9.05
Contractor 4	9.25
Contractor 5	9.95

Case 1: lowest bid
Lowest bid method
Winning bid £8.65 m submitted by Contractor 1

Case 2: average of all bids, closest to the average
Average of all bids = £9.22 m
Winning bid (closest to the average) £9.25 m, submitted by Contractor 4

Case 3: average of bids excluding outliers, closest below the average
Average of all bids excluding highest and lowest = £9.1 m
Winning bid £9.05 m submitted by Contractor 3

In some parts of the world clients expect to use the lowest one or two tenders submitted as a starting point for further negotiations to reach the final price. While there is nothing inherently wrong with negotiation to reduce the price where the tender exceeds the available budget, the process becomes unethical when employers attempt to negotiate simultaneously in a 'Dutch auction' with the two or three lowest tenderers in order simply to drive down the price. This process would in any event seem to be counter-productive in the long run since:

1. Tendering contractors rapidly get to know that this is the case and one would expect their mark-up to include an allowance for subsequent negotiations.

2. Negotiation on a price submitted in a genuine competition adds considerably to the uncertainty for tendering contractors and might therefore be expected to lead to unstable bids.

14.12   CHOOSING THE BEST BUY WHEN MULTIPLE CRITERIA ARE INVOLVED

The previous discussion has dealt solely with projects where there is only a single decision variable, i.e. the contract price. However, developments in procurement methodologies and dissatisfaction with the possible undesirable

Table 14.4 Example of multi-criteria tender bids

Tender list	Bid price (£m)	Time required
Contractor A	1.05	42 weeks
Contractor B	1.20	38 weeks
Contractor C	0.985	52 weeks
Contractor D	1.16	36 weeks

consequences of 'low-bid' methods are leading informed clients away from the 'traditional' lowest bid approach. In the words of John Carlson of Massachusetts Institute of Technology, quoted in Torricane (1993), 'As owners become more sophisticated, the traditional process will be seen for what it really is: usually high risk for all at unacceptable levels of service'. Torricane gives a useful indication of American progress:

> The US Army Corps of Engineers is forsaking the low bid on some projects, in the hope of reducing the staggering number of claims and disputes attached to its projects (about 850 claims per year totalling more than US$1 billion in fiscal years 1991 and '92 combined.)

It is therefore necessary to examine how the 'best buy' can be chosen where more than one variable is involved. The simplest case might be where tenderers are asked to quote both a price and also the time required to carry out the works.

Consider the tender bids shown in Table 14.4. In this case the client is faced with a classical dilemma. Does it pay more to have the building finished early, or less and get the building later? Decisions such as this are very difficult, and will be related to the client's financing package (i.e. the way the project is to be financed and the financing charges that must be paid) and to the potential gain involved in having the building earlier. Additional information in the form of discounted projected cash flows may help.

Inviting tenders on this kind of basis is not uncommon, but is fraught with problems, not only for the client but also for the tendering contractors. It has already been shown that there is a range of possible prices which a contractor could bid for the work, and that these prices are to some extent related to the construction period. Without some guidance from the client the tendering contractors have no idea whether the client's prime need is for speedy completion or lowest price. It is not therefore a good idea to invite tenders on the basis of multiple criteria unless the client is at least able to give the tendering contractors some idea of where its priorities lie. It would be far better to invite all tenders on the basis of a common predetermined contract period and to ask tenderers to quote an alternative price on the basis of shortest possible completion. At least then the client has some common measure against which to judge all tender submissions.

The problem of multiple decision criteria becomes more acute still when non-traditional procurement methods are used, for example when using variants of the design and build approach. In this case the client is trying to decide not only upon price and construction period but also on the quality of the design and the functionality of the building. In all but the simplest of cases it will be in the client's best interest to appoint its own professional team of conventional specialists (e.g. architect, quantity surveyor, engineers) to assist it with the preparation of the brief and to advise it on the relative merits of the various submissions. One common approach is for the professional team to develop the brief with the client and on that basis to prepare a list of criteria against which the various submissions are to be judged; remember that in the case of a substantial design and build scheme in the UK there are only likely to be a few (perhaps only three or four) submissions. It is common for each of the criteria to be given a weighting, and for them all to be combined into a simple linear model of the type given earlier:

$$AR_j = \sum_{i=1}^{n} (W_i)(R_{ij})$$

where

AR_j = aggregate rating or 'total score' for scheme j

n = total number of decision criteria in the model

W_i = weighting given to decision criterion i (sum $W_i = 1$ for $i = 1...n$)

R_{ij} = rating given to scheme j for criterion i

Experience seems to show that it is likely that, unless the process is carefully controlled, the number of criteria identified by the team might be very large. One scheme for a new design and build hospital in Scotland is reported as having had 304 separate assessment criteria (McTaggart, 1993). The greater the number of criteria the more difficult it is likely to be to reach a decision. It is also highly likely that the tendering process will be prolonged, and would be likely to include one or more presentations in addition to a documentary submission.

The simple model set out above is quite crude. It assumes that each of the decision criteria are separately and independently assessable and that their scores are simply additive. This may not be the case (for example cost, time and quality are inextricably linked). Again, the professional skill would seem to lie in the weightings allocated to each of the criteria. This process is seen as crucial, otherwise it could be argued that the best that such a model could produce would be likely to be the least inspiring and most conservative solution to the problem. Nonetheless, models of this type are used, successfully it would seem, but it is obviously important that the decision criteria and the weightings associated with them need to be very carefully considered. Paek *et al.* (1991) describe the development of a fuzzy logic-based computer system for the evaluation of design and build proposals.

This approach, however, assumes that all of the decision criteria are mutually independent and can each be separately identified, weighted and scored. Clients are, however, usually searching for an integrated approach to the solution of their problem: a contractor who can grasp the broad picture, the full implications of all of the problems posed and provide an innovative, effective and coherent strategy to overcome them. In this case a decomposed view of definitive attributes each with its own rigid weighting might not identify the best solution, whereas a holistic view might. Consider the case of the US$140 m US National Archives Building reported by Torricane (1993). In this case, in addition to price, bidders were asked to provide:

> ...a list of personnel who would work on the project, submit resumés and references for those people and indicate whether staff would work full-time or part-time on the job. The General Services Administration, the contracting agency, also asked bidders to describe exactly how they would attack the complex job from a technical perspective.... Hyman [the successful contractor] also included in its bid a list of the major subcontractors it would use on the project, and details of its own financial and corporate history.

The methods used in practice, in the main, for the evaluation of multi-criteria construction bids are crude and unscientific. Although workable processes and procedures have been available for almost 20 years in other disciplines, their use in construction is still in its infancy. The disciplines of management science and social science have developed some very sophisticated techniques to aid multi-criteria decision-making under conditions of uncertainty. Green (1992, 1994) provides a concise introduction to multi-attribute decision theory, and discusses the use of the Simple Multi-Attribute Rating Technique (SMART) and its later derivatives SMARTS and SMARTER (Edwards, 1977; Edwards *et al.*, 1988; Edwards and Barron, 1992). In the context of value management, there is surely scope for further research into how these and other similar techniques could be practically applied in the evaluation of construction bids.

14.13   FEEDBACK

It has already been shown that contractors base their assessment of market trends and current market prices largely on feedback from their various tender submissions. Feedback to tendering contractors from the tendering process is therefore essential. It is recommended by some that clients should make available to tendering contractors a complete list of all tenders received for each project let. For public sector projects this would seem to be an essential part of public accountability. Many contractors, however, do not wish their competitors to be able to identify which bid is theirs, and it is therefore more common for clients to release to each tenderer a list of the tender bids received with no names attached, and this is the procedure recommended by the NJCC Code of Procedure for Single Stage Selective Tendering. This would seem to be acceptable, in that each tendering contractor can then identify how its own bid compares both with the successful tender and with the overall range of tender prices.

Feedback of this kind from the client is not, however, always forthcoming, particularly from the private sector, and contractors therefore sometimes rely more on informal feedback routes. It may be argued that informal feedback is just as good as formal feedback from the client, but informal networks rely on the contractor knowing who all of its competitors are, and this may not be easy for a large project with a wide geographical spread of firms.

14.14   CONCLUSION

This chapter has examined the client's needs and objectives with regard to the competitive tendering process. It has been shown that the client's prime objective should not merely be to get the lowest price for the work, and that in many ways other criteria are more important.

The chapter has also examined some of the methods and techniques used in the prequalification process, and has examined a variety of alternative methods of assessing submitted tenders. It is clear that while considerable research in these areas is taking place there is apparently still plenty of scope for further research work in the UK.

14.15   REFERENCES

Altman E.I. (1968) 'Financial ratios, discriminant analysis, and the prediction of corporate bankruptcy', *Journal of Finance*, Vol. 23, No. 4, pp. 589–610.

Altman E.I. (1973) 'Predicting railroad bankruptcies in America', *Bell Journal of Economics and Management*, Vol. 4, No. 1, pp. 184–211.

Diekman J.E. (1981) 'Cost plus contractor selection', *Journal of the Technical Councils*, American Society of Civil Engineers, Vol. 107, pp. 1211–25.

Drew D. (1993) 'A critical assessment of bid evaluation procedures in Hong Kong', *Professional Builder*, Chartered Institute of Building (Hong Kong Branch), June 1993, Hong Kong.

Drew D. and Skitmore M. (1992) 'Competitiveness in bidding: a consultant's perspective', *Construction Management and Economics*, May 1992, pp. 227–47.

Edwards W. (1977) 'How to use multi-attribute utility measurement for social decision making', *IEEE Transactions on Systems, Management and Cybernetics*, pp. 326–40.

Edwards W. and Barron F.H. (1992) *SMARTS and SMARTER: Improved simple methods for multi-attribute utility measurement*, Social Science Research Institute, University of Southern California.

Edwards W., von Winterfelt D. and Moody D.L. (1988) 'Simplicity in decision analysis: an example and a discussion', in *Decision Making: Descriptive, Normative and Prescriptive Interactions* (ed. Bell D.), Cambridge University Press, Cambridge MA.

Elsam R. (1826) *The Practical Builder's Perpetual Price Book*, Kelly, London.

Flanagan R. and Norman G. (1989) 'Pricing policy', in *The Management of Construction Firms* (eds. Hillebrandt P.M. and Cannon J.), pp. 129–53, Macmillan, Basingstoke.

Green S.D. (1992) *A SMART methodology for value management*, Occasional Paper No. 53, Chartered Institute of Building, London.

Green S.D. (1994) 'Beyond value engineering: SMART value management for building projects', *International Journal of Project Management*, Vol. 12, No. 1, pp. 49–56.

Herbsman Z. and Ellis R. (1992) 'Multiparameter bidding system – innovation in contract administration', *Journal of Construction Engineering and Management*, Vol. 118, No.1, pp. 142–50, American Society of Civil Engineers.

Ioannou P.G. and Leu S.S. (1993) 'Average-bid method – Competitive bidding strategy', *Journal of Construction Engineering and Management*, Vol. 119, pp. 131–47.

Kangari R., Farid F. and Elghar H.M. (1992) 'Financial performance analysis for construction industry', *Journal of Construction Engineering and Management*, Vol. 118, No. 2.

Langford D., Iyagba R. and Komba D.M. (1993) 'Prediction of solvency in construction companies', *Construction Management and Economics*, Vol. 11, pp. 317–25.

Lenard D.J. (1991) 'Building company failures', in *Management, Quality and Economics in Building* (eds. Bezalga A. and Brandon P.S.), E. & F.N. Spon, London.

McTaggart R. (1993) 'In the pink; West Fife DGH – the procurement process', *Hospital Development*, August 1993, pp. 19–21.

Nguyen V.U. (1985) 'Tender evaluation by fuzzy sets', *Journal of Construction Engineering and Management*, Vol. 111, pp. 231–43.

Paek J.H., Lee Y.W. and Napier T.R. (1991) 'Selection of design/build proposal using fuzzy logic system', *Journal of Construction Engineering and Management*, Vol. 118, No. 2, pp. 303–17.

Potter K.J. and Sanvido V. (1994) 'Design/Build pre-qualification system', *Journal of Management in Engineering*, Vol. 10, No. 2, pp. 48–56.

Powell C.G. (1980) *An Economic History of the British Building Industry*, Architectural Press, London.

Russell J.S. (1992) 'Decision models for analysis and evaluation of construction contractors', *Construction Management and Economics*, May 1992, pp. 185–202, E. & F.N. Spon, London.

Russell J.S. and Jaselskis E.J. (1993) 'Predicting construction contractor failure prior to contract award', *Journal of Construction Engineering and Management*, Vol. 118, No. 4, pp. 791–811.

Russell J.S. and Skibniewski M.J. (1990) 'QUALIFIER-1: contractor pre-qualification model', *Journal of Management in Engineering*, Vol. 116, No. 1, pp. 155–69.

Russell J.S., Skibniewski M.J. and Cozier D. (1990) 'QUALIFIER-2; knowledge based system for contractor pre-qualification', *Journal of Construction Engineering and Management*, Vol. 116, No. 1, pp. 155–69.

Simon (1944) *The Placing and Management of Building Contracts*, Chairman Sir E. Simon, HMSO, London.

Tam C.M. (1993) Discriminant Analysis Model for Predicting Contractor Performance in Hong Kong, *PhD Thesis*, Loughborough University of Technology, UK.

Young B.A. (1991) 'Corporate failure in the construction industry', in *Management, Quality and Economics in Building* (eds. Bezalga A. and Brandon P.S.), E. & F.N. Spon, London.

15 Consortium and Joint Venture Bidding

15.1 INTRODUCTION

The terms 'consortium' and 'joint venture' are often used in connection with construction work, particularly for large and/or complex projects, many of which are located in the less developed areas of the world. Involvement in such projects may pose particular problems for construction contractors because:

1. The projects themselves are often both large and complex, and may pose special risks in terms of their cultural, geographical and political environment.

2. Most tenders for construction work are usually prepared by one company acting alone and in competition with other similar firms, and most construction contractors are therefore not accustomed to tendering as part of a team

3. A substantial number, perhaps most, consortia and joint venture organisations are set up to handle specific one-off projects, and it is therefore usually necessary to re-establish the necessary management and administrative organisations afresh for each new project.

4. An increasing number of consortium and joint venture projects also require the joint venture sponsor to arrange the necessary finance to carry out the work.

It is therefore evident that the risk element in joint venture/consortium arrangements is usually much more complex than in a traditional tendering situation. This chapter considers some of the more important issues that arise for contractors participating in joint venture or consortium projects, particularly during the pre-contract stage.
The following questions are considered:

What do the terms 'joint venture' and 'consortium' mean in the context of contractors bidding for work?

Why would companies wish to join together to bid for projects?

What are the requirements for a successful joint venture?

What are the potential pitfalls?

What are the principal methods of project financing and what problems might they pose?

15.2 JOINT VENTURES AND CONSORTIA

A consortium may be simply defined as a grouping of firms or individuals gathered together for the accomplishment of some specific purpose, for example the execution of a construction project. There have been a large number of attempts to define the term 'joint venture', but according to Torrance *et al.* (1992), one of the best definitions is that published by the Association of General Contractors of America in their Joint Venture Guidelines:

A joint venture is a pooling of assets and abilities of two or more firms for the purpose of accomplishing a specific goal on the basis of showing profits or losses'.

Although it could be argued that a 'joint venture' can be composed of only two firms, whereas, by definition, a 'consortium' would imply a group composed of more than two, it is nevertheless reasonable in the present context to consider the two terms to be, for all practical purposes, synonymous. Many large joint ventures are formalised by the establishment of a separate company to carry out the joint venture project, with each of the participants having an agreed stake and taking a proportionate share of the risks, liabilities, profits and losses.

The possible range of complexity of joint venture construction projects is very wide. On a domestic level, for example, a contractor might join forces with consultants in private practice and perhaps with selected specialist subcontractors to prepare submissions for a design and build project. Alternatively, in the international arena a property developer/contractor in one country might join with a local landowner in another country for the purposes of foreign investment. Perhaps the most complex arrangements are those required for multi-party international projects such as the Channel Tunnel. In this particular project 10 contractors were involved grouped into two separate consortia, one British and one French, which themselves then combined to form one consortium which acted as the main design and build contractor for the project. Seeley (1984) describes how the Department of Health and Social Security has used many joint venture schemes, comprising a building contractor and a mechanical and electrical contractor to tender for and carry out the work as joint main contractors.

In addition to the complexities posed by the parties, further complications can arise where the project sponsor also undertakes to provide finance. In these cases the range and type of financial arrangements can be extremely imaginative and almost infinitely variable to suit local conditions. Projects in the Third World often require imaginative arrangements. Walker and Flanagan (1987), for example, quote the following three types of joint venture arrangement for foreign firms wishing to invest in China:

1. Equity joint ventures, which are effectively firms jointly invested in and managed by a foreign firm and a mainland Chinese organisation and in which the risks, profits and losses are generally shared in accordance with the equity stake of the partners.

2. Cooperative ventures, where a foreign partner and a mainland Chinese partner enter into a contract, generally for the completion of some specific project, for example a building. In this case the liabilities, rights, profits, risks and obligations of the parties are enshrined in the contract document.

3. Compensation trade, where mainland Chinese enterprises buy technology or equipment, for example a factory, from foreign firms on credit, with the initial principal and interest being paid off over some future period out of the revenues from the products produced.

There are many other types of innovative financing, often supported by governments, and some more ethical than others. The examples quoted give some idea of the range of options.

15.3 ADVANTAGES OF A JOINT VENTURE OR CONSORTIUM ARRANGEMENT

Although this chapter is principally concerned with the pre-contract considerations of joint venture deals, it is first necessary to understand why construction companies should want to enter into this type of arrangement.

There are many reasons why a firm might want to enter into some form of collaboration with others. Some of the most important are described below.

To Allow Penetration Into New International Markets Which are Not Accessible to the Firm Unless it Has a Local Partner
This is fundamentally important in a number of areas of the world, particularly in countries where the home government wishes to exercise a high degree of

control over the operation of the economy and of the amount of foreign investment allowed, and/or where it wishes to encourage some element of technology transfer. This situation was, until recently, typified by the People's Republic of China, where foreign investment was only allowed as part of a joint venture with a local Chinese partner. It is therefore obvious that if a foreign firm wishes to enter markets of this kind it *must* do so in partnership with a local organisation as part of a joint venture deal.

To Allow the Firm to Broaden its Base by Competing in Markets Where it
Does Not Have All of the Requisite Skills, Knowledge or Experience
This can be a useful marketing strategy. An example might be where an established construction company with considerable experience in specific sectors of the industry wishes to expand its operations into other niche markets. In this case entering into a joint venture agreement with another, possibly smaller, firm which already has experience in the target market can be mutually attractive. In this case, one partner gets an introduction to the new market while the other partner gets access to the resources and expertise necessary to become involved in larger and more complex projects.

A further example might be where a firm wishes to prepare a design and build bid for a large project. In this case contractors may enter into a joint venture deal with consultants (architects, engineers, quantity surveyors etc.) and specialist subcontractors in order to prepare a bid for a specific project. In cases such as this, and particularly when the construction industry is depressed, consultants will sometimes be prepared to work on a 'no job, no fee' basis, drawing their fees from the contractor only if the bid is successful. The contractor is thus able to share the cost of preparing the bid, and hence spread the risk of losses in the event that the bid might not be accepted, with others in the consortium.

Aside from those countries where joint venture partnerships with local organisations are mandatory if foreign firms wish to enter the market, other countries have adopted a policy to encourage joint ventures between foreign and local contractors by other means. Lam (1990), for example, quotes a number of cases in South-East Asia where, in addition to the local partner's invaluable knowledge of the local construction industry, customs and bureaucracy, the foreign contractors have also typically received generous financial incentives. In return, the local firms have been able to take advantage of technology transfer in the form of learning new management skills and construction techniques, which have, in turn, improved and upgraded the skills of the local construction industry.

The Economist (1990) reported that there have been a number of instances of international joint ventures in Europe in recent years as a result of the increasing degree of economic integration of the European Community partners, and in some cases firms have formed even closer strategic alliances through mergers and acquisitions. This 'internationalisation' of the construction industry can give rise to some strange results. Betts and Ofori (1992), for example, report that:

> The phenomenon is leading to a complex web of cross-country inter-linkages and 'incestuous' relationships. For example, as at mid July 1990, Dumez, a French building contractor, owned 34% of Belgium's CFE, 10% of Dawidag of West Germany (which owned 5% of Dumez itself) and 5% of Alfred McAlpine of the UK. Phillip Holzmann of West Germany owned 50% of Josta (Spain), 14% of Nord France, 14% of Tilbury (UK) and all of Hillen and Roosen (Holland).

To Allow the Firm, in Combination with Others, to Tender for Extremely Large and Complex Projects

Construction projects in the international arena are becoming increasingly large and more complex. Examples of typical recent 'mega-projects' would be the Channel Tunnel and the works related to the construction of the new airport at Chek Lap Kok in Hong Kong. It would be very doubtful whether any one company would have either the financial resources or the necessary construction skills to tackle projects of this size and complexity, and even if it did the risks involved would be far too great for any one firm acting alone to carry. It therefore makes sense for a group of specialist contractors with complementary skills to form a consortium to tender for projects of this type.

Consider, for example, the consortium formed for the construction of the Channel Tunnel. The main contractor in this case was Transmanche-Link (TML), who were awarded a contract to design, construct and commission the whole transport system. TML was a joint venture between two separate consortia, one British (Translink) and one French (Transmanche Construction). Each of these consortia in turn consisted of five construction companies, as follows:

Translink	*Transmanche Construction*
Balfour Beatty Construction Ltd	Bouygues SA
Costain Civil Engineering Ltd	Dumez SA
Tarmac Construction Ltd	Société Auxiliaire D'Entreprises SA
Taylor Woodrow Construction Ltd	Société Générale D'Entreprises SA
Wimpey Major Projects	Spie Batignolles SA

In the case of the British consortium each of the members provided finance, management expertise and specialist knowledge, and each held a 10% stake in the project as a whole. Profits and losses were therefore to be shared equally among the consortium members (Young, 1992). This project also highlights the point that no one company was big enough to take on the whole project. Young (1992), reporting on a case study of the project, makes the point that:

> The five UK joint venture companies when combined had 21% of the UK construction industry which in 1990 came to £48.467 billion. This is an indication that no one company alone could take on the Channel Tunnel contract by itself, which when it was awarded stood at £4.7 billion (1985 prices) and is currently worth £9 billion (1992 prices). Average turnover per day for TML is a staggering £3 million which reinforces the use of joint ventures.

Elsewhere in the world the concept of risk sharing through the medium of joint ventures is common even for quite small projects. Lam (1990), for example, points out that in Japan a large proportion of all construction work is carried out by joint ventures. He further points out that in some cases the joint venture may be concealed from the client in that the client signs a contract in the normal way with one construction company which, in turn, has an informal agreement with a number of joint venture partners to share the work, together with any profits or losses. To the client, therefore, these parties appear to be merely domestic subcontractors. The potential for fraud and deceit is only too obvious.

To Exploit Or Create Previously Untapped Market Opportunities

Many areas of the developing world lack both the infrastructure necessary to support sustained economic growth and also the financial resources required to procure the necessary infrastructure. Typical examples would include roads, railways and electric power generation facilities.

This issue has been largely addressed by construction-based consortia developing imaginative variations on the build–own/operate–transfer (BOT) model. According to Augenblick and Custer (1990), the acronym BOT was first coined in the early 1980s by the late Turkish Prime Minister Turgut Ozal, but the origins of the technique can be traced back to the French use of '*le concession*', such as that granted to the Perier brothers to provide a water distribution system for Paris in the late 18th century. Under this type of arrangement the consortium usually forms a separate company which then undertakes to construct the relevant facilities and also to provide the necessary development finance. In return, the developer is granted a concession to operate the completed facility as a profit-making entity for some agreed period of time, typically 10–30 years, with an obligation to maintain the facility during this period. At the end of the concession period the whole facility is handed over to the host government at no cost in full working order.

A growing number of examples exist. Walker (1993) identifies over 80 projects of this type in 22 countries which are either proposed, operating or in the course of construction. Many are toll roads, tunnels or bridges, but there is a growing market for projects of this type in the provision of public utility services. An example is the 700 MW Shajiao B power station in southern China, constructed between 1985 and 1987 under the terms of a joint venture between a Chinese Government-backed body, Shenzhen Special Economic Zone Power Development Co. and Hopewell Power (China) of Hong Kong. In this case the Chinese party provided the land and some local expertise, while Hopewell provided for design, construction and maintenance of the plant and arranged the necessary finance. The joint venture agreement provides for Hopewell to operate the station for a period of 10 years, buying coal from and selling power to the Chinese authorities at prearranged prices. In this case the construction contract was arranged by Hopewell between the joint venture company and a separate consortium of contractors consisting of Mitsui and Co. (commercial leader), Toshiba Corporation (technical coordinator and generator islands), Ishikawajima-Harima Heavy Industries (boiler island) and Slipform Engineering, itself a Hopewell subsidiary (architectural, civil engineering and building work).

The financial arrangements for this scheme will be considered in more detail later, but the above brief description is sufficient to indicate the complexity of the contractual and financial arrangements necessary for the successful completion of projects of this sort.

15.4   REQUIREMENTS FOR A SUCCESSFUL JOINT VENTURE

The first and most important requirement for a successful joint venture is that the project must be economically and technologically viable. Given these criteria, the requirements for a successful joint venture partnership are much the same as those for any other kind of partnership, and indeed for any construction project. The following have been identified by Sanvido *et al.* (1992), Torrance *et al.* (1992), Tiong *et al.* (1992), Tiong and Yeo (1993) and Smith and Walker (1994), among others, as being some of the main 'critical success factors' (Rockart, 1982), applicable to construction projects and joint venture arrangements.

A Well-organised Cohesive Team
The development of a strong 'team chemistry' must be developed through the pursuit of common goals and activities. It could be argued that the prime aim in all construction joint ventures should be to achieve a high degree of synergy, a situation where the combination of the separate factors is brought together in such a way that the eventual result achieved is greater than the sum of the parts. Young (1992), in her case study of the Channel Tunnel project, makes the point that:

Synergy is the driving force and is essential because it can make the difference between the success and near success of a project.

Implicit in this idea is the notion that there must be mutual trust between the various parties and mutual agreement about what the eventual goals actually are. In order that these things can come about, a number of supporting mechanisms are also required. Essentials would include good communication links, good managers and management skills and a true willingness to participate in a shared activity for the benefit of all involved. Some of these things can prove difficult to achieve, particularly when personnel are seconded to the joint venture on a part-time basis while still being employed within their parent companies. The need for strong, sensitive and professional management of the joint venture vehicle is clear if the potentially disparate elements of the team are to be successfully welded together into a cohesive unit.

Precise and Comprehensive Contracts and Agreements

Another important consideration is that the risks, costs and benefits of the project are shared equitably among the members of the consortium. This factor is obviously of vital importance in the case of very large projects, where the cost of preparing the bid can in itself be huge. Torrance *et al.* (1992) suggest that the partners to the joint venture should each have equal shares. While the rationale for this is easy to see, it is apparently not necessarily a prerequisite. Young (1992), for example, reporting on the French joint venture involved in the Channel Tunnel scheme reports that:

Two of the member companies had a larger stake than the other three. Bouygues SA had a bigger stake then the rest. This was mainly due to its financial size and its ability to take on more responsibility and risk than the other four companies. The three smaller companies were more specialised and concentrated on certain technically demanding sections of the work.

It seems that each joint venture should be looked at individually, and it would seem reasonable to structure the agreement in such a way that the company able to take the biggest share of the risk should also take the biggest share of the potential rewards. It is evident that a series of well-drafted contracts and agreements is essential. The agreements must be drawn in such a way that they define precisely the roles and obligations of each of the parties, together with the allocation of their respective risks, rights, liabilities and benefits, but which also encourage the various participants to behave as a team without conflicts of interest or differing goals. The drafting of such agreements is obviously a very demanding task.

Relevant Knowledge and Experience

The selection of suitable partners for a joint venture is of paramount importance. Together, the various members of the consortium must possess all of the expertise necessary to complete the project but without unnecessary redundancy, and they must all be prepared to work together for the good of the team as a whole.

Many joint venture bids are put together by groups of people either on the basis of personal contacts or by firms who have worked successfully together in the past. As an example, consider the case of the joint venture team which submitted the successful design and build bid for a major hospital project in Scotland. In this case the initial opportunity was identified by an architect in private practice, who then approached a personal contact employed by a large building contractor which he knew had extensive experience in the construction of major hospitals. The building contractor brought on board mechanical and electrical subcontractors and consultants with whom it had worked successfully before, and assumed the lead role of 'bidder' for the project. Structural engineering and quantity surveying consultants were also added to the team.

15.5   POTENTIAL PROBLEM AREAS FOR JOINT VENTURE AGREEMENTS

15.5.1   Management Issues

The main potential sources of friction between the parties to a joint venture agreement are relatively easy to identify. Many potential areas of conflict, particularly those relating to arguments over individual members' contributions and obligations, together with their share of potential risks, benefits and liabilities can and should be forestalled through careful drafting of the joint venture agreement, but there may be other potential areas of conflict which are not so easy to foresee. Among the more important identified by Torrance *et al.* (1992) are:

1. Divided loyalties, where managers assigned to the joint venture may feel that the interests of the joint venture as a whole conflict with the interests of their parent company.

2. Attempted interference in the management and decision-making process of the joint venture company from individual parent companies.

3. Changes of policy inside the joint venture members' parent organisations may lead to attempts to change the terms of the joint venture agreement. This may be especially important in the case of joint ventures involving governments, such as those set up as build–operate– transfer projects. These projects are extremely sensitive to political

stability, and a change of government policy can result in very serious disruption of the joint venture agreement. A historical example is that of the Suez Canal, opened in November 1869 under the terms of a 99 year concession from the Egyptian government, but which was later nationalised before the end of the concession period. A more recent example concerns the new Bangkok Expressway. In this case, part-way through the construction period, the Thai Government unilaterally changed the conditions of the concession such that the operators, who hold a 30 year concession, would only be allowed to collect two-thirds of the toll agreed in the original contract. Foreign bankers were not amused.

Less extreme and perhaps more common examples of governmental interference might include changes in taxation policy or financial controls, or political instability.

4. Lack of trust between the joint venture partners can reduce the efficiency of the management and decision-making processes, and can also lead to partners being wary of sharing information, techniques and technology. It is conceivable that there might be particular problems here in the case of international joint ventures where cultural differences between the parties, if not fully appreciated and understood by all concerned, could give rise to considerable misunderstanding and consequent lack of mutual trust. Swierczek (1994) uses a case study approach investigating a number of mono- and multicultural groups in South-East Asia to analyse how issues of culture can create conflict within large projects such as international joint ventures. Differences of perception, values, attitudes and expectations must be identified early on in the venture, and agreements must be reached which are accepted by all parties to be a fair compromise by all concerned. Torrance *et al.* (1992), reporting on the preliminary results of research into national and international joint ventures, report that:

> In particular, with regard to the cultural dimensions of joint ventures, the findings are emphasising the need for greater understanding of and allowances for two main cultural dimensions. That is, the external cultural features of the societies from which the joint venture partners are drawn. It is essential to clearly distinguish those common features of beliefs, values and attitudes which generally exist within the different cultures. In addition, the professional ethics and practices, together with normal business practices must be identified arising from each culture. Where differences exist, these must be clearly understood and accepted by all the parties involved and agreement reached over how

allowances are to be made in order to accommodate these differences.

Young (1992) however, in her description of how the cultural differences issue was apparently successfully resolved in the Channel Tunnel project, appears to indicate that the issue was not really a problem at all:

> It is apparent that no special arrangement was made between the UK companies in order to accommodate cultural differences in language, technology and managerial approach of the French contractors.... To ensure that business practices between the British and French companies were as compatible as possible, exchanges of personnel were cultivated while accepting that there were differences in culture and attitudes.

It would seem that the important thing is to explore, in as much detail as possible, what cultural differences might cause problems before signing the joint venture agreement.

15.5.2   Commercial Issues

Reference has already been made to the need for the joint venture agreement to identify and record each party's contribution to the venture, and their respective shares of the potential risks, profits and losses. These are issues upon which each party must make its own detailed assessment prior to commitment to the venture. It is therefore vitally important that each party evaluates these factors from its own purely selfish point of view, and in order that this may be done the joint venture sponsor, usually the 'lead bidder', must provide all of the necessary information.

In the case of a simple joint venture, such as that for the submission of a design and build bid, the decision might be relatively easy. The possible loss to a participating consultant, an architect for instance, will be limited to its costs incurred in preparing the necessary design information, and it must balance this potential loss against the probability of its consortium submitting the winning bid. Its assessment of whether or not its consortium stands a good chance of submitting the winning bid will be governed by its assessment of the other partners, particularly perhaps the lead bidder, and also by its assessment of the strength and number of competitors.

For contractors entering into a long-term joint venture, for example a BOT arrangement, the risks are much more difficult to assess. Typical potential risks listed by Li (1993) include:

1. Construction risk, including time delays, cost overruns etc.

2. Infrastructure problems, including the availability of transport links and public utility services. This is especially important in the case of projects in the developing world.

3. Market risks, including the availability of raw materials, accuracy of market demand forecasts and stability of the market price for the project's product.

4. Political risk, including taxation, financial controls, labour relations regulation and political stability.

5. Operating risk. This will require a comprehensive life cycle cost study of the operation and maintenance costs of the project.

6. Foreign currency risks. The entire stability of the project may be threatened by unexpected currency fluctuations affecting the prices of imported or exported goods and materials. Such fluctuations can have serious effects upon the project's ability to service the debt. Foreign currency exposure in developing countries is a major concern.

7. Insolvency risk, including insolvency of the sponsor, joint venture partners and suppliers.

All of these factors will require the preparation of a detailed financial model, upon which the sensitivity of changes to any or all of these factors can be tested. Computer-based techniques, such as Monte Carlo simulations, can be used to examine the probable consequences of changes in the key variables.

Parties to joint ventures of this type will typically attempt to limit their risk exposure through the formation of a separate joint venture company, which will assume the whole of the liabilities of the project and in which the principal partners to the deal will simply be shareholders. The company will be established in such a way that, in the event of the joint venture incurring losses, there is only limited recourse to the parent companies' assets.

15.6   PROJECT FINANCING

It is common for contractors involved in long-term joint ventures such as BOT projects to undertake to arrange the necessary project finance as a part of the overall deal. This is an extremely complex area and only an outline can be given here.

In principle, the problem is simple, in that the financing package must initially provide sufficient finance to cover the costs of constructing the facility, with the debt being repaid over the period of the concession out of the income generated. In practice, however, the need for the funding institutions to limit their own risk exposure and to be reasonably sure that the loan will indeed be repaid means that the detailed arrangements for a large BOT scheme may be extremely complex.

Most financing packages will consist of a mix of equity, that is, contributions to the cost of the scheme raised from shareholders in the joint venture company, and debt raised from commercial sources. Commercial sources could include government development banks, export credit agencies, pension funds, insurance companies and commercial banks. Many developed countries operate some kind of export credit guarantee scheme to help their own exporters to win overseas projects. Williams (1993) explains that the national export credit agencies basically do this through the provision of finance in support of contracts for which their exporters are bidding, and that this is usually done by providing long-term fixed interest rate finance. This can obviously soften the risks which a joint venture company might be exposed to in respect of fluctuations of interest rates over time. Williams (1993) also explains the role of the merchant banks in arranging project finance as the 'putting together of those who have finance with those who need it, and structuring a transaction'.

Walker (1993) and Tiong and Yeo (1993) report that the equity percentage in joint venture schemes of this type seems generally to fall within the range of 10–30%, although they also point out that there are schemes where the percentage falls well outside this range. Examples are the Shajiao B power station in the People's Republic of China (3% equity) and the Sydney Harbour Crossing in Australia (5% equity). The Dartford Bridge Crossing in the UK has no equity component at all. In many cases the winning bid for BOT projects, particularly in the developing world, has been the one which has offered the most imaginative and advantageous financing package.

One example of innovative financing is the case of the Standard Chartered Bank in Hong Kong, where the bank effectively procured its new building for no capital outlay. In this case the bank granted a 25 year lease on the site to Nishimatsu Property (Hong Kong), a subsidiary of the Nishimatsu Corporation. Nishimatsu in return financed the construction cost of the bank building and paid a premium. The agreement provided for the bank to have the exclusive rights to lease back 70% of the completed building for the 25 year lease period at a fixed rental, while Nishimatsu has the right to let out the remaining 30% at market rates. At the end of the 25 year lease period ownership of the entire building reverts unconditionally to the bank.

International joint venture arrangements in Third World countries often introduce further complications, particularly in the case of currencies which are not freely convertible on the money markets. Consider for example the financial arrangements for the Shajiao B power plant constructed in China. In this case the concession period was for 10 years, from 1988 until 1998. The initial development finance was raised partly from shareholders and partly in the form of syndicated bank loans. The loans themselves were partly in Hong

Kong dollars, partly in Japanese Yen and partly in Chinese Renmenbi, all secured basically by the assets of the joint venture company and with only limited recourse to the assets of the parent companies, to be repaid in instalments during the concession period. Part of the assets of the joint venture company were an offtake agreement to supply power and a coal supply agreement, under the terms of which the major Chinese joint venture partner agreed, for the period of the concession:

1. To take and pay for not less than 60% of the installed capacity of the plant in each year at predefined prices, half in Chinese Renmenbi (not at that time convertible on the open market) and half in other currencies (principally Hong Kong dollars and Japanese Yen) converted from Renmenbi at predetermined exchange rates.

2. To provide coal to an agreed quality standard again at predefined prices.

15.7   CONCLUSION

Joint venture contracting is becoming increasingly popular as projects become larger and more complex, and as contractors try to find more and better ways both to share the risks inherent in the construction business and to expand their own markets into the developing world. The rewards to be gained from joint ventures are potentially very large, but the risks are large too, and the financial arrangements can be very complex. A careful evaluation of the economic and managerial soundness of joint venture proposals is therefore essential before entering the field.

15.8   REFERENCES

Augenblick M. and Custer B. (1990) 'The build, operate and transfer approach to infrastructure projects in developing countries', *Working Papers*, World Bank, August 1990.
Betts M. and Ofori G. (1992) 'Strategic planning for competitive advantage in construction', *Journal of Construction Management and Economics*, Vol. 10, pp. 511–32.
Lam T.I.P. (1990) *Report on a critical comparison of the construction procurement and contracting systems in Japan, Singapore, Malaysia and Hong Kong*, Hong Kong Polytechnic.
Li W.Y. (1993) Construction management strategies for capital investment projects with special reference to China, *Unpublished MSc Dissertation*, City Polytechnic of Hong Kong.
Rockart J.F. (1982) 'The changing role of the information systems executive: A critical success factors perspective', *Sloan Management Review*, Vol. 24, No. 1 pp. 3–13.

Sanvido V., Grobler F., Parfitt K., Guvenis M. and Coyle M. (1992) 'Critical Success Factors for Construction Projects', *Journal of Construction Engineering and Management*, Vol. 118, No. 1, pp. 94–111.

Seeley I.H. (1984) *Quantity Surveying Practice*, Macmillan, Basingstoke.

Smith A.J. and Walker C.T. (1994) 'BOT: Critical factors for success', *Proceedings of the International Conference on Investment Strategies and the Management of Construction*, Croatia.

Swierczek F.W. (1994) 'Culture and conflict in joint ventures in Asia', *International Journal of Project Management*, Vol. 12, No. 1, pp. 39–47.

Tiong R.L.K., Yeo K.T. and McCarthy S.C. (1992) 'Critical success factors in winning BOT contracts', *Journal of Construction Engineering and Management*, Vol. 118, No. 2 pp. 217–29.

Tiong R. and Yeo K.T. (1993) 'Project financing as a competitive strategy in winning overseas jobs', *International Journal of Project Management*, Vol. 11, No. 2, pp. 79–86.

Torrance V.B., Ali M.Y.I., Fatani A.J. and Smith A. (1992) 'Research into national and international joint venture projects of U.K. Construction companies', *Project Management International Conference, Guangzhou, China – Proceedings*.

The Economist (1990) 'Builders take their partners for Europe', *Economist*, 14 July 1990, pp. 63–4.

Walker A. and Flanagan R. (1987) *China: Building for Joint Ventures*, Levett and Bailey, Hong Kong.

Walker C.T. (1993) BOT Infrastructure: Anatomy of Success, *Unpublished MSc Dissertation*, City Polytechnic of Hong Kong.

Williams M.F. (1993) 'Provision of finance – merchant banking and export credits', *Project Management International Conference, Guangzhou, China – Proceedings*.

Young B.A. (1993) 'A joint venture in the UK construction industry – the Channel Tunnel', *Project Management International Conference, Guangzhou, China – Proceedings*.

16   Computers in Estimating

16.1   INTRODUCTION

The main purpose of this chapter is to discuss the various ways in which computer systems can be used by contractors in estimating, tendering and associated functions. It is not intended to provide an introductory course in computing, and it is therefore assumed that the reader will already be familiar with the basic components of a small desktop computer, and be competent to use, for example a simple word processor.

16.2   COMPUTERS IN ESTIMATING

The use of computers for estimating by construction contractors has a long, if somewhat chequered, history in the UK. By the early 1970s a number of the larger national contractors had written their own estimating systems to run on large in-house mainframe computers, and the general introduction of interactive computing and, later, microcomputers through the 1970s meant that by the beginning of the 1980s a number of vendors were offering microcomputer-based estimating packages for general sale. The number of packages on offer mushroomed during the 1980s. Ewin and Oxley (1985) report that in April 1984 there were 38 systems available on the market, but by 1986, Wager (1986) reported 90 different packages available.

Unfortunately, many of the early packages were not very good, and response from contractors was not particularly enthusiastic. In common with many other early computer systems developed for the construction industry, many estimating packages required their users to modify and standardise their methods of working to suit the shortcomings of both the rather primitive computers (by modern standards) then available, and also to compensate for the poor understanding of the process shown by many early system developers. Estimating has always been an individualistic and idiosyncratic activity, and this requirement for change in operating methods coupled with the need to learn how to use an often unfriendly computer system virtually guaranteed that many early systems would fail to achieve any great popularity. Many estimators therefore decided that computers were not for them, and elected

227

to continue to work manually, and a substantial number of those firms who did decide to follow the computer route ignored the packages on offer in the market-place in favour of building their own systems. The result was that in 1987, Peat Marwick McLintock, in their annual construction industry survey for the Construction Industry Computing Association (CICA) (Peat Marwick, 1987) reported that around 40% of those contractors using computer-based estimating systems were using systems developed specifically to suit their own purposes rather than systems bought 'off the peg'. Even as late as 1990 the CICA annual survey (Peat Marwick, 1990) still showed that only 52% of construction estimators surveyed used computer-based methods.

So perhaps the first question to ask is: why use computers for estimating at all?

16.3   WHY USE COMPUTERS FOR ESTIMATING?

The introduction of computer-based techniques to any process is inevitably a trade-off between costs and savings. Computer systems are expensive, and their introduction usually involves a substantial learning curve. Introduction of a computer system must therefore pay for itself either in terms of time or cost savings or in terms of an improved tender success rate. At the lowest end of the cost scale, estimators can make considerable use of general purpose spreadsheet software for unit rate analysis etc., but spreadsheets do have their limitations. On the other hand, fully fledged special purpose estimating software tends to be expensive but offers a wider range of capabilities.

The reasons most often given for the introduction of computer based estimating software are:

Speed
Most estimating system suppliers claim that their software will speed up the estimating process in that the systems will automatically extend quantities and rates, and total pages, collections and summaries with 100% arithmetical accuracy first time. Overall estimate preparation time is therefore reduced because of the elimination of the arithmetical checking associated with manual estimating.

Consistency
The estimating software usually includes some provision for a library of resource costs, standard production times, plant rates etc. This may either be supplied by the system supplier in a form which can be modified and updated by the user as required, or be generated by the particular user either from basic principles or from previous projects. In this latter case the estimating system comes basically as a shell. The system can, therefore, if required, take the place of the estimator's ubiquitous 'little black book'. Use of some sort of standard information can at least give a consistent basis

for estimate production, both from one estimate to another and also across estimators working in the same office.

Flexibility

The information used to generate estimates prepared using computer systems can usually be represented very easily in a wide variety of different forms to suit different uses. Examples might include various forms of resource-based analysis, bill of materials analysis and cost code analysis. In addition, many computer systems provide easy methods of distributing the mark-up around the estimate in a variety of different ways in order to generate the final priced bill of quantities.

Integration

Some estimating systems will interface with other software for valuations, contract costing etc., thus enabling reuse of the estimator's data for budgeting and post-contract purposes.

16.4   AVAILABLE OPTIONS

While some large construction companies might still use estimating systems based on large central computers, most computer applications in estimating would nowadays be implemented on personal computers, probably most often used as standalone machines, but increasingly linked together into local area networks, thus allowing data to be shared among several people. This can be useful in a large organisation with a number of estimators, all of whom might wish to share some common library of information. Although the organisation and mechanics of the computer system are important as far as the firm as a whole is concerned, and will form a main plank of the firm's computing policy, what is of interest here is the estimator as user of the machine, and an in-depth discussion of computing policy issues is beyond the scope of the present work. Smith (1989) gives a good introduction to the wider aspects of computing policy.

There are basically three options available to estimators wishing to implement a computer based system, namely:

1. General purpose software (spreadsheets, databases, etc.)

2. Purpose written software

3. 'Off the shelf' estimating software

16.4.1   General Purpose Software

This section is concerned with the use of general purpose software specifically for estimating, and while estimators will, in common with almost everyone else, probably have a need for general word processing, the subject is not considered here. The types of general purpose software which are likely to be of specific use to estimators are spreadsheets and database management systems.

Spreadsheets

A spreadsheet is essentially a computerised representation of a large sheet of paper divided vertically into columns and horizontally into rows. Each row is numbered and each column is lettered. The intersection of each row and column is called a cell, and each cell can be uniquely addressed by giving the column letter and row number. Each cell can contain text, a number or a formula deriving the contents of that particular cell from the contents of other cells. Figure 16.1 shows a part of a simple spreadsheet to calculate the total hourly cost and the cost per trowel for bricklaying gangs of various combinations.

In Figure 16.1, cells A1, A3, A4, B6 and B8 all contain text, while cells B3, B4, C3 and C4 contain numbers input by the user. Cells D3, D4, D6 and D8, however all contain formulae, and the figures printed in these cells are derived from the numerical information. Cell D3, for example contains the formula B3*C3 (* means multiply), and D3 is therefore set to a value corresponding to the number in cell B3 multiplied by the number in cell C3. Similarly, cell D4 contains the formula B4*C4. Cell D6 contains the formula D3+D4, and thus the value is the sum of the values in cells D3 and D4, while cell D8 contains the formula D6/B3 (/ means divided by), so that the total hourly cost in cell D6 is divided by the number of working bricklayers in cell B3 to give the hourly cost per trowel for the gang as a whole. Any changes made to the

	A	B	C	D
1	Bricklaying gang rates			
2				
3	Bricklayer	3	6.57	19.71
4	Labourer	1	5.54	5.54
5				
6		Total per hour		25.25
7				
8		Cost per trowel		8.42

Figure 16.1   Simple spreadsheet example

values for the number of bricklayers and labourers (cells B3 and B4) or the hourly costs per man (cells C3 and C4) will automatically cause the total cost per hour and the cost per trowel to be recalculated.

⌞Spreadsheets provide a very wide range of built-in mathematical and logical functions which mean that commonly used calculations can easily be set up as standard templates for use with any job-specific input data.⌝Commonly used unit rate calculations, for example, can be set up as standard sheets with price and productivity data being inserted for each project as required. Spreadsheets are also very good for performing 'What if?' simulations, allowing rapid testing of many different alternatives with different sets of data. It is, however, a mistake to view spreadsheets in too simplistic a way. The logical functions provided in most systems allow spreadsheet packages to be used as programming languages in their own right. Weber (1987), in using a spreadsheet to create an expert system, draws attention to the wider possibilities:

> All too often spreadsheets are treated as if they were only fit for accounting and financial forecasting. Even the simplest spreadsheet is a limited form of language while the more sophisticated ones are powerful and versatile programming languages in their own right. Their control structures tend to be limited, but they do offer many advanced functions that would take a great deal of coding in other languages.

Some spreadsheets allow the data to be considered in a three-dimensional form (i.e. as a book of pages allowing transfer of data between pages) rather than as a single two-dimensional sheet.

Spreadsheets are very easy to use, and useful results can be achieved with very little effort even by a complete novice. As the user's skills develop, increasingly more complex operations become possible. Spreadsheets can therefore form the ideal introduction to computers for those estimators who are yet to be convinced of their potential usefulness. Brook (1988) provides a good introduction to the use of spreadsheets in estimating.

Spreadsheets do, however, have some limitations, in that while it is possible to carry out complex calculations and to transfer information between different spreadsheets, to do so requires considerable expertise. They also require that the user spend an appreciable amount of time setting up, testing and debugging the standard templates in the first place, and this operation becomes increasingly more time-consuming as the sheets become more complex. The importance of this task cannot be overemphasised. It is all too easy to make silly errors when setting up the spreadsheet, and the errors become more difficult to spot as the sheet becomes more complicated. Since people seem to have an in-built tendency to believe anything which appears on a computer printout almost without question, careful checking of the early results is vitally important.

Most spreadsheet programs will theoretically allow sheets of several hundred columns by several thousand rows, but in practice the size of sheet is limited by the memory capacity of the computer.

Database Management Systems

Perhaps the most widespread use of computers today, certainly in the commercial world, is for the storage and manipulation of information. The storage capacity of modern computer systems means that even small desktop microcomputers can store, analyse and manipulate very large quantities of information. Simply put, a database is just a structured file of information, which is stored in the computer such that it is generally accessible in a variety of ways. Each file contains a series of records, each of which is analogous to an individual card in a card index system, and each record is composed of a number of separate data items.

This type of system can be used by estimators for a wide variety of purposes. Examples might be subcontractor and supplier records, drawing and tender registers, and various types of cost data. Betts (1987) proposes the use of a micro-based database package for the collection and analysis of information by building contractors for use during the tendering process.

Most database management packages are easy to use at an entry level, and estimators should quickly be able to build fairly simple but useful systems. Like many other things, however, they become much more difficult as the user attempts to do more complex things, and an extensive database will require detailed design on paper before attempting to set up the system. Among the questions which need to be asked are:

1. How will I keep track of all of the information stored in the system?

2. In what different ways am I likely to want to access and present my information?

In other words: how is the data to be indexed? Database management systems support multiple indexes, allowing the data to be retrieved in many different ways, but the indexing systems often have to specified when the database is created. This problem obviously becomes more acute the larger the collection of information, and if the information is to be used by more than one person (for example a centrally maintained company file of subcontractor and supplier information) the administrative problems involved in controlling both access to and updating of the information become more difficult to resolve satisfactorily as the number of users increases. There is therefore the need to establish a logical structure for storage of the information.

Only collections of information organised in this kind of highly structured way truly deserve to be known as 'databases', and a wide variety of software tools have been designed specifically to organise and manipulate such databases, ranging from simple electronic 'card index' systems suitable for use on the smallest of microcomputers up to very large systems designed for use on large mainframe machines. Large systems, even those implemented on desktop microcomputers, also present significant computing problems in order to ensure efficient storage of the information and optimum speed of access. Such problems become especially critical as the number of users grows and their reporting and presentation requirements become more complex, and some very involved methods of referencing the relationships between the various pieces of data have been devised. Databases organised on this kind of model are termed 'relational', and the definitive work in this area is encapsulated in a set of twelve rules formulated by Dr Edgar Codd. Codd's rules, summarised in Hares (1988), form an outline specification for a truly relational database.

One of the fundamental requirements for a good database management system is that the user should be able to interrogate the database in a language similar to that used for natural speech. True natural language interaction with computers, at least at the interrogative level, still remains a dream, although considerable research has been carried out in this field. Each of the database management systems presently available includes some interpretation of a natural query language (indeed the language used for the Software AG product 'Adabas' is even called 'Natural'), and such programming languages have been termed 'fourth generation languages', often abbreviated to 4GL. Fourth generation languages as a class are very powerful and provide extremely clever ways of manipulating the information stored in the database with considerably less effort and within a much shorter time than was possible with earlier programming languages.

The introduction of a multi-user database poses particular management problems in that different users might need to be allowed different 'rights' to access and update the information. Information stored in a large database is likely to represent a considerable investment in terms of time spent collecting it, and any organisation will naturally want to protect the database from unauthorised alteration by users, while still allowing the data to be read. Alternatively, some parts of the data may be particularly sensitive, and one might need to restrict some users' access rights while still allowing access to other non-sensitive data. Most systems allow the data to be protected by various levels of security, and management must decide what database administration and security procedures are appropriate for each particular installation or organisation.

The development of complex databases is a specialised task, and would normally fall within the realm of a software professional.

16.4.2   Purpose-Written Software

The development of purpose-built in-house software packages is a substantial task. It is invariably very expensive and is hardly ever completed within the originally set time and cost parameters. It is a task which should normally only be considered as a last resort when all other options have been explored and rejected. Unfortunately, however, this exploration process is often merely a cursory glance, and in many cases companies are discouraged by the apparently high prices of available software packages; there is always the feeling that it will be cheaper and in some way 'better' if the system is developed in-house using staff already on the payroll or, worst of all, by an enthusiastic amateur. All too often, new converts to the use of computers become almost addicted to developing increasing more complex and involved systems, often in their spare time, and this tendency can easily encourage management to believe that useful software will result. It rarely does. Few good estimators (or quantity surveyors or contracts managers) become even half-competent software authors, and anything they do produce, even if it initially appears to produce impressive results, will usually be idiosyncratic, be generally unstructured, always be poorly documented, and be virtually impossible to maintain.

The purpose-built alternative therefore, although it might at first sight appear to be cost-effective often proves to be a false economy. Gooding (1988) sums up the issue very well:

> A great many companies look inside for solutions. They are still prepared to develop their own systems when a step back from the problem would tell them that reinventing the wheel is wasteful. Packages are more than trouble free code; they represent an investment in someone else's experience.

The time-scale for major software developments from inception to implementation is usually measured in years. Some idea of the process and potential time-scale for a major purpose-built system can be gleaned from Steel (1991), in which he describes the development of an estimating system for Balfour Beatty. The best advice to give to estimators thinking of developing their own software is 'Don't', although Ewin and Oxley (1985) make the point that in some cases, for particular specialised applications, purpose-built software may be the only feasible choice.

16.4.3   Off the Shelf Estimating Packages

Following the boom of the mid-1980s, the number of estimating packages on the market has now declined and stabilised somewhat, although the range is still broad. The majority of packages now on the market have been available for long enough for the 'bugs' to have been found and removed, but don't expect any system, no matter how well tried, to be totally error free. *Flight International* magazine for example, reporting the case of an Airbus airliner which made a very heavy landing in a storm in Hong Kong in mid-1994, stated that the pilot's problems were partly caused by inappropriate advice given by the aircraft's computer systems due to the fact that the particular combination of weather conditions encountered had not been foreseen when the software was written. Even the best designed and most carefully tested systems have flaws.

Packages vary considerably both in price and in the facilities offered. The most basic systems will provide unit rate build-ups from files of basic resources, together with automatic extension of quantity and rate and totalling of pages, collections and summaries. Some systems provide a measurement facility, often accompanied by a comprehensive library of standard items somewhat akin to an electronic price book. This is obviously useful for plan and specification projects, where the contractor has to prepare its own quantities. Some systems also provide scanning facilities to allow the bill of quantities to be scanned directly into the contractor's computer, where text recognition software will turn the image into a text file for direct input to the estimating program. While this facility can be useful, it does rely on clean unmarked copies if the text is to be read accurately. A better solution, which is just beginning to be used, is for the bill to be distributed both as a text file on floppy disk, which can be read directly into the contractor's software, and in conventional printed form.

The traditional view of the relationship between estimating, tendering, budgeting and cost control is shown in Figure 16.2.

Some estimating packages, however, may also be combined with other modules to form a comprehensive integrated contractor's financial management system. Integration of estimating into the financial management process means that contractors can then achieve the truly integrated approach shown in Figure 16.3.

Following an in-depth study, O'Brien and Pantouvakis (1993) conclude that none of the existing systems presently on the market have been shown to be generally acceptable to the majority of estimators. They go on to report the development of a set of estimating tools which are, they claim, capable of meeting the individualistic character of the estimating process.

Faced with the apparently bewildering array of systems on the market, the question which then arises is how contractors choose the package best suited to their specific needs.

16.5 CHOOSING THE RIGHT PACKAGE

A common problem with the introduction of computers... is deciding how to go about it. There are pressures from the press, salesmen, often

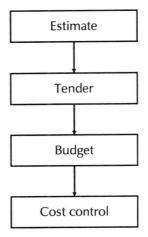

Figure 16.2   The traditional view.

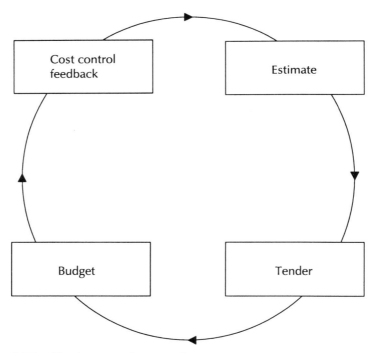

Figure 16.3   The integrated approach.

from staff, and from attitudes of 'keeping up with the Jones'. The first steps are often difficult, usually the most crucial, invariably the ones with the most pitfalls.

The above quotation is taken from an influential study carried out by the Construction Industry Computing Association (CICA, 1981) published almost 15 years ago, and yet the sentiments are just as true now as they were then. Choosing the right system is a difficult problem, particularly if the organisation has not used computers for estimating before. It may be that the organisation already has computers of some kind, and one constraint may be to find some software which will run on existing equipment. This is usually feasible, particularly if the equipment is fairly new, say less than two years old, but in general it is a bad idea to start with the hardware and try to find software to fit. A much better plan is to choose the software first and then buy the software and hardware as a package. There is some merit in buying the whole package from one supplier; if the system fails, regardless of whether the failure is in hardware or software, you only have one person to chase!

Choice of the right software is crucial. Arditi and Suh (1991) make the point that:

...many firms purchase systems that do not provide the correct combination of features. The cost and frustration of making the wrong decision is apparent in the time and effort lost in training, modifying company routines, and going through the same process again with a different package; confidence in computerized estimating may be shattered for ever.

Usually the choice will be a balance between the estimator's 'wish list' of features that he or she would like to have balanced by the amount the firm is prepared to pay, and an essential prerequisite is to spend some time looking at what is available in the market-place. Once you have an idea of what is available, make a list of the features the ideal package should contain, but do not be seduced by gimmicks.

Aside from obvious questions like what hardware is required, some general questions to be asked when you begin looking at systems seriously might be:

1. *How easy is it to use? How difficult is it to break? How understandable are the instructions and the error messages?*
These questions are vital. Computer systems are supposed to help people, not hinder them, and the system should help the user to get the most out of it. Menus and error messages should be clear and unambiguous. Managers should not rely on the salesperson's demonstration or even on their own opinion. Get an opinion from the person who will actually be expected to use the system. Talk to other users. Ask the supplier for a list

of some existing users and talk to them, but be careful: do not forget that people are sometimes reluctant to admit that they have made a mistake!

2. How well supported is the system, both hardware and software? How good is the documentation? Is there a 'user hotline'? Is there an active users group? How much does the maintenance cost? How much are upgrades?
Maintenance charges are often expensive. Hardware suppliers usually have a range of charges depending upon the required response time. Software maintenance varies from excellent to non-existent, usually depending upon the price range of the package. Some of the cheaper PC-based packages are sold 'as is', with virtually no warranty or maintenance support.

The documentation provided with many systems is often difficult for inexperienced users to understand, and the supplier should be a lifeline in case of trouble. It must therefore not only have a good understanding of the package, but must also be able to respond quickly and effectively to users' queries and problems. This may mean either a telephone hotline or a physical presence sufficiently close to the user's office for a consultant to sort out the problem. All too often the software supplier has to fax the problem to somewhere else for a solution.

A good question to ask is, 'Who would I call if I have a problem with my system at lunchtime on Christmas Eve and I have an urgent job to be completed that day?'.

3. How much training is required/included in the cost of the system?
Proper training is essential for a complex system, even if it does seem expensive. It is false economy to buy an expensive system and then skimp on the training costs. It is also, in general, a big mistake to think that you can install a system, give someone the manual and let them learn to use it by themselves. Remember to allow time for the users to become familiar with the system without the day-to-day pressure of a busy estimate production schedule. It is just not realistic to expect to install a system today and have everyone competent to use it on operational work tomorrow.

The problem of choice of estimating system is considered by Arditi and Suh (1991), who developed an expert system designed to advise on the choice of estimating software based on a number of factors, including the number of bids submitted per year, the characteristics of the projects to be tendered, and the estimating team environment (number of people in a team, specialisation etc.)

16.6 MANAGEMENT OF THE SYSTEM

In addition to the actual use of the equipment by the estimator, consideration needs to be given to both the firm's overall computing policy and the way in which the computer system is managed. In policy terms, decisions need to be taken about whether the company will allow each member of staff to operate essentially alone, as shown in Figure 16.4, or whether the firm should encourage a more integrated approach, as shown in Figure 16.5. In the first case users all have standalone computers and carry the responsibility for looking after their own data, but the disadvantage is that common data cannot be easily shared, thus making life potentially difficult if a number of estimators are all working on the same project. Use of the integrated approach, however, carries the added overhead that someone has to manage and control the shared data files.

A similar argument applies to the place of the estimating function within the operation of the firm as a whole. The simplest approach is for each discipline – estimating, quantity surveying, planning, etc. – to operate its own self-contained systems, whereas an integrated approach would link all systems into some kind of network with centrally maintained project files accessible to all.

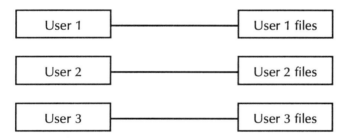

Figure 16.4   The piecemeal approach

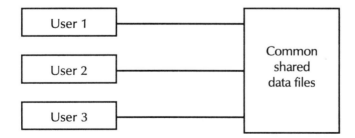

Figure 16.5   The integrated approach

The above gives only a very brief overview of some of the problems of computer systems management. The subject is complicated and involved, and the problem becomes increasingly acute as the installation grows larger. An in-depth consideration is beyond the scope of this text, but Smith (1989) includes further discussion of some of the major issues. Smith and Kelly (1991) discuss the human factors to be considered in gaining the maximum potential from the implementation and use of computer systems.

The other important issue to be considered is to do with security of the data. The information stored in a computer system may represent several person years of effort, and in the case of a company which relies heavily on its computer systems the loss of the data could be catastrophic. Information actually in the computer, either on hard disk or floppy, is under threat from a number of sources including:

Physical damage caused by faulty machinery, for example a defective disk drive might physically damage the disk.

Corruption of the data due to a faulty programme, the inadvertent introduction of a computer virus, or electrical surge caused by lightning strike, power failure etc.

Operator error causing accidental destruction or corruption of data files.

Physical damage from some outside cause, for example fire or flood.

In addition, floppy disks can also easily be corrupted while not in the computer by stray magnetic fields, heat generated by sunlight through a window, use of the disk as a coffee mat etc.

The most common way of protecting data is to take security copies of files at regular intervals. The frequency and extent of the copies will vary depending upon the importance of the data and the frequency with which it is updated, but most careful users of hard disk systems will take a complete 'dump' of the hard disk perhaps weekly, either onto floppy disks or cartridge tape, with regularly used and important files being copied to floppy disk every day. This single copy arrangement at least ensures that in the event of a disaster the system can be recreated from some known point in time. Note, however, that with this arrangement only the original and one copy of the data exist, and thus while the copy is being taken both copies of the data are in the computer at the same time. Any potential problem which might occur during the security copying process could therefore destroy both the original and the only copy. A common approach is to use at least two separate security copies in rotation, thus leaving at least one copy outside the computer at any one time.

Remember also to store backup copies safely. In the event of, for example, a fire in the office, it is not a lot of use having backup copies of everything if the backup copies were stored in a plastic box on top of the computer.

16.7 TENDERING

The use of computers in estimating has been largely a matter of automating the existing manual processes, and the computer techniques employed have been those derived from commercial data processing. Some, however, have attempted to use computers as aids to decision-making in the tendering process.

Park and Chapin (1992) publish a computer program called Databid, which uses a variant of the statistical probability bidding model as the basis of a decision support system designed to advise contractors about optimum mark-up levels based on past results. A floppy disk containing a basic version of the Databid software is included with their textbook, together with operating instructions. The authors claim that (Park and Chapin, 1992, p. 242):

> The Databid system... is offered as a simple, practical, and proven approach to developing an effective data-based competitive bidding strategy.... The overall objective of the Databid system is simple: to make as much profit as possible on each job bid, based on the job characteristics and the prevailing competitive situation.

Other researchers have attempted to use newer and more experimental computing techniques to try to model the human decision-making process. Tam *et al.* (1994) present a fuzzy logic-based model which attempts to derive an optimum mark-up percentage based on a set of rules derived from the factors considered important in tendering as shown by the response to a survey of contractors in Hong Kong. Paek *et al.* (1993) report a similar approach, using fuzzy set theory in the pricing of construction risk.

Another group of researchers has attempted to go further and to create computer systems which 'learn' by mimicking the way people learn and which can then provide advice in the manner of a human expert. Such systems have become known as 'expert systems'.

16.8 EXPERT SYSTEMS

The concept of 'artificial intelligence', the construction of an 'intelligent' machine, is a subject which has captured the hearts and minds of people for hundreds of years. In the main of course, such things lie in the realm of science fiction, but in the years since the end of the Second World War the pursuit of 'artificial intelligence', AI for short, using computers has become a widely researched area of study.

In order to make any sense of the concept it is first necessary to define what 'intelligence' actually means. Typical dictionary definitions speak of 'quickness of understanding', 'intellect', 'capability for rational thought' etc.; words which even given the most liberal of meanings could not be applied to any computer system yet in existence or even foreseeable in the near future. Despite the fact then that a considerable body of so-called artificial intelligence research now exists, the word 'intelligence', in this context, generally implies nothing more than an ability in some sense to 'learn'; that is to say that the computer system is able to evaluate the results of its own actions and to modify its own behaviour in order to ensure that incorrect or invalid actions or responses are not repeated. Simple examples might, for instance, include a computer-controlled industrial robot equipped with impact sensors which is required to perform some sequence of operations in a factory. Such a device could be made to modify its own behaviour pattern by taking input from the sensors whenever contact was made with some adjacent object, and using that information could construct a 'map' of its surroundings in order to prevent accidental collisions. The machine can thus be said to have 'learned' from its own experience and in some limited sense to have displayed some intelligence. Another example might be a computerised version of the guessing game 'Animal, vegetable, mineral', where the computer attempts, on the basis of answers to questions asked, to deduce the identity of some object, animal, plant etc. by means of a decision tree. In the event of an incorrect guess the system can 'learn' by asking how it could discriminate between the incorrect guess and the correct answer, and the new information is then added to the computer's internal decision tree.

Such examples are trivial and yet they do indicate the extremely wide range of artificial intelligence research.

Perhaps the most widely acclaimed offshoot from artificial intelligence research has been the development of a range of computer software, based on specialist knowledge, which attempts to reach some conclusion, to solve some problem, by means similar to those employed by a human expert. Such systems have become known as 'expert systems'. The first computer program to be explicitly recognised as an expert system was probably DENDRAL, a system developed at Stanford Research Institute from about 1965 onwards for the inference of chemical structures from mass spectrometer readings.

Perhaps the most definitive definition of an expert system is that approved by the British Computer Society Committee of the Specialist Group on Expert Systems reported in d'Agapeyeff (1983):

An expert system is regarded as the embodiment within the computer of the knowledge based component from an expert skill in such a way that the system can offer intelligent advice or take an intelligent decision about a processing function. A desirable additional characteristic which many would consider fundamental is the ability to justify its own line or reasoning in a manner directly intelligible to the enquirer. The style adopted to attain these characteristics is rule based programming.

Lansdowne (1982) discusses the potential for the use of expert systems on construction, Wager (1984, 1985) contain good reviews of the use of expert systems in construction as a whole, and Hamilton (1985) discusses the possible use of expert systems in building services. It is, however, in quantity surveying that perhaps the most significant strides have been made to date. The first publicly available expert system in the estimating field was Elsie, a program designed to provide initial cost advice for building developments marketed by the Royal Institution of Chartered Surveyors and described in Brandon *et al.* (1988).

A number of other researchers (Gaarslev, 1991; Moselhi *et al.*, 1993; Hegazy *et al.*, 1994) have described expert system programs designed to simulate the bidding process, mainly using computers configured as neural networks. Although initial results were not encouraging, the author believes that, in time, these lines of research will prove beneficial.

The effect which the widespread use of expert systems and the like will have upon the professions has been the subject of much comment and discussion. Evans (1979), for example, wrote at length about the professions' probable decline of influence as the use of computer-based information systems becomes more widespread.

In the final analysis, estimators and other professionals must accept and embrace the spread of 'smart' computer systems; to consider doing otherwise would be as foolish as Canute attempting to halt the tide. The introduction of such systems is not a threat but an opportunity to transcend those highly structured rule-based tasks for which the computer provides an acceptable alternative in favour of those much less structured, and usually more reward-ing, tasks involving the exercise of human judgement.

16.9   INTEGRATED SYSTEMS

Reference has already been made to the fact that some organisations are beginning to issue bills of quantities for tender purposes on floppy disk as well as in printed form which contractors can then download into their own estimating systems. In addition, the extraction of quantities from CAD models is, in principle, straightforward, although not necessarily in the form required by the various Standard Methods of Measurement. Some system developers are also looking at the possibility of linking information in the CAD model with time scheduling and planning software, and although historically the development of large-scale integrated systems has not been particularly successful, present efforts to establish commonly acceptable data exchange standards for CAD model data do represent a way forward, in that they will eventually make possible the ready exchange of information between disparate computer systems. It has also already been shown that the conventional bill of quantities is not a particularly good tool for the contractor to use in pricing construction work because it does not generally relate well to construction techniques and site processes. In addition, time pressure during estimating and tendering often precludes the contractor from testing and evaluating alternative construction methods and techniques. What is required from the contractor's point of view, particularly in the case of large and/or complex schemes, is a method of easily and quickly simulating construction of the building by a variety of techniques in order to find the most economic approach.

Perhaps in the future the bill of quantities in its present form will no longer be required. All that will be required is for the architect to deliver to the contractor a copy of the CAD model in computer-readable form. The contractor, using its own software, could then retrieve from the model all of the information required to carry out 'What if?' simulations and to prepare its tender in whatever form it considers to be appropriate.

There is also considerable interest in some parts of the world in applying the computer-integrated manufacturing techniques developed in manufacturing engineering, where CAD information is used to control machinery and equipment in the manufacturing process, to the construction industry. The process has been christened computer-integrated construction (CIC), and is being enthusiastically embraced in Japan. Yasuoshi Miyatake, Senior Managing Director of the Technical Division of Shimizu Corporation wrote, in 1993, that (Miyatake and Kangari, 1993):

Construction companies that emphasise CIC are likely to gain a significant competitive advantage over those that do not.

Miyatake and Kangari go on to describe the development of a test-base prototype system integrating CAD, construction planning, cost control and financial planning with a site automation system called SMART (Shimizu Management system by Automated Robotic Technology). The site automation system handles, plans and assembles prefabricated components for medium- to high-rise steel-framed buildings using robots controlled by a real-time computer system. Miyatake and Kangari report that, in future, Shimizu plan 'to advance the system further to reduce the labor and construction period to one-half of the traditional method'. Neither is Shimizu alone. Other large Japanese contractors, including Taisei Corporation and Obayashi Corporation, are reported to be working on similar systems. Miyatake and Kangari conclude that:

In the next decade, implementation of CIC is expected to play an important role among the large Japanese construction companies.

16.10   REFERENCES

Arditi D. and Suh K. (1991) 'Estimating system expert selection', *Journal of Construction Management and Economics*, Vol. 9, pp. 369–81.

Betts M. (1987) 'A co-ordinated system of information retrieval for building contractor's tendering', in *Building, Cost Modelling and Computers* (ed. Brandon P.S.), E. & F.N. Spon, London.

Brandon P.S., Basden A., Hamilton I. and Stockley J. (1988) *Expert systems: the Strategic Planning of Construction Projects*, Royal Institution of Chartered Surveyors, London.

Brook M. (1988) *The use of spreadsheets in estimating*, Technical Information Service No. 97, Chartered Institute of Building, London.

CICA (1981) *Chartered Surveyors and the Micro-computer*, Royal Institution of Chartered Surveyors, London.

d'Agapeyeff A. (1983) *Expert Systems, Fifth Generation and UK Suppliers*, National Computing Centre, Manchester.

Evans C. (1979) *The Mighty Micro*, Coronet Books, London.

Ewin N. and Oxley R. (1985) 'An estimating system for a medium sized speculative building firm using fourth generation software', in *Information systems in Construction Management* (ed. Barton P.), B.T. Batsford, London.

Gaarslev A. (1991) 'Neural networks – technique tested on classical bidding strategy data set', in *Management, Quality and Economics in Building* (eds. Bezalga A. and Brandon P.S.), E. & F.N. Spon, London.

Gooding C. (1988) 'Time for the proof of the pudding', *Computer Weekly*, 18 February, pp. 26–7.

Hamilton G. (1985) *Expert systems in building services*, Paper presented at the Construction Industry Computing Association Annual Conference.

Hares J. (1988) 'Tapping the trends', *Informatics*, February, pp. 68–70.

Hegazy T., Moselhi O. and Fazio P. (1994) 'A neural network approach for representing implicit knowledge in construction', *The International Journal of Construction Information Technology*, Vol. 1, No. 3, pp. 73–86.

Lansdowne J. (1982) *Expert systems: their impact on the construction industry*, Royal Institute of British Architects Conference Fund, London.

Miyatake Y. and Kangari R. (1993) 'Experiencing computer integrated construction', *Journal of Construction Engineering and Management*, Vol. 119, No. 2.

Moselhi O., Hegazy T. and Fazio P. (1993) 'DBID: Analogy based DSS for bidding in construction', *Journal of Construction Engineering and Management*, Vol. 119, No. 3, pp. 466–79.

O'Brien M.J. and Pantouvakis J.P. (1993) 'A new approach to the development of computer aided estimating systems for the construction industry', *Construction Management and Economics*, Vol. 11, No. 1, pp. 30–44, E. & F.N. Spon, London.

Paek J.H., Lee Y.W. and Ock J.H. (1993) 'Pricing construction risk: fuzzy set application', *Journal of Construction Engineering and Management*, Vol. 119, No. 4, pp. 743–56.

Park W.R. and Chapin W.B. (1992) *Construction Bidding*, John Wiley, New York.

Peat Marwick (1987) *Building on IT*, Construction Industry Computing Association, Cambridge.

Peat Marwick (1990) *Building on IT for the 90s*, Construction Industry Computing Association, Cambridge.

Smith A.J. (1989) *Computers and Quantity Surveyors*, Macmillan, Basingstoke.

Smith A.J. and Kelly G. (1991) 'Beating the people factor', *Chartered Quantity Surveyor*, September, pp. 15–16, Royal Institution of Chartered Surveyors, London.

Steel R. (1991) 'The BBEST approach to computer aided design', in *Applications of Information Technology in Construction* (ed. Maxwell J.W.S.), Thomas Telford, London.

Tam C.M., Lam K.C. and So A.T.P. (1994) 'The effect of risk management on bidding strategy in the construction industry: the fuzzy reasoning approach., *Proceedings: Third Regional Conference*, Chartered Institute of Building Services Engineers, Australia.

Wager D. (1984) *Expert Systems and the Construction Industry*, Construction Industry Computing Association, Cambridge.

Wager D. (1985) *The Future of Expert Systems in Construction Management*, Construction Industry Computing Association, Cambridge.

Wager D. (1986) 'First generation estimating', *Construction Computing*, April, pp. 12–30, Chartered Institute of Building, London.

Weber J. (1987) 'Working to rule', *Personal Computer World*, June, pp. 130–3.

Index